STOICHIOMETRY

Atomic Weights, Molecular Formulas, Microcosmic Magnitudes

This book is in the ADDISON-WESLEY SERIES IN THE PRINCIPLES OF CHEMISTRY

Consulting Editor, FRANCIS T. BONNER

STOICHIOMETRY

Atomic Weights, Molecular Formulas, Microcosmic Magnitudes

LEONARD K. NASH *Kollender*, *1918-*

Department of Chemistry

Harvard University

ADDISON-WESLEY PUBLISHING COMPANY

READING, MASSACHUSETTS · PALO ALTO · LONDON · DON MILLS, ONTARIO

Preface

"To measure the elements" is the literal meaning of stoichiometry (Gr. *stoicheion*, element + *metrein*, to measure). Apart from the physicists' fundamental particles, atoms and molecules appear to be the "elements" most distinctive of chemical thought today. We may, then, properly use the word stoichiometry to signify the general inquiry that permits chemists to weigh and number atoms and molecules. Only a rather hasty overview of this inquiry is ordinarily offered in the secondary-school course in chemistry. Some justification can be offered for the superficiality of this introductory treatment, but, in my opinion, there is every justification for seeking to do better at the college level. The present text thus takes as its primary goal a systematic examination of how—by assigning weights (or masses) to atoms and formulas to molecules—chemists become able to characterize the fundamental entities of chemistry.

The present account is not historical, but it focuses on a classical problem. How, starting from data for macroscopic systems only, can we attain to reasonably secure knowledge of the (chemical) microcosm? This problem can, of course, simply be by-passed—by beginning at once with electrons, nucleons, mass-spectrometric data, and the like. One then approaches the subject along the very popular "high road," a route which seems to me to have some objectionable concomitants. This whole approach is founded on data the students cannot themselves collect (or even see collected, data obtainable only by the use of complex instruments the construction of which is not detailed, data rigorously interpretable only with the aid of theories known to the beginning student very incompletely if at all. A treatment that takes its foundation here cannot but encourage an uncritical faith in data that are no more than announcements, and an uncritical acceptance of arguments that are too often wholly lacking in logical force. I cannot believe that the prospective scientist benefits from the encouragement of such attitudes.

v

I have chosen a more traditional approach to the subject, setting out from several conspicuous regularities in the combining weights of elements and in the general deportment of gases. One then follows the "low road." The intellectual atmosphere is, perhaps, less immediately exhilarating; but one entirely avoids the clouds of mystification through which the high road must often proceed. The low road is no doubt a very *pedestrian* route, but just that is its most notable virtue. The student's feet rest solidly on the bedrock of data he can (or could) himself collect, data obtainable with the simplest apparatus, data *almost completely* interpretable by straightforward applications of precisely those theories that are central to the subject of chemical stoichiometry. *Almost completely*, but not quite. To avoid complications in several derivations from the kinetic theory, I have made some calls on "faith"—but such appeals are clearly flagged and few in number. And, to avoid making a long story even longer, I have used the customary oversimplifications in discussing data obtained from mass spectrometry, etc.,—but, no longer the central foundation of the entire argument, these data now figure only as welcome confirmations and extensions of conclusions already drawn from an argument founded on solider ground.

From his study of this book, the student should expect to gain full mastery of a coherent set of modes of thought and calculation. Important in its own right, this mastery will stand him in good stead in his later studies of such subjects as chemical equilibrium. The student ought to gain some acquaintance with a variety of experimental methods—most notably, a number of simple techniques for the approximate determination of molecular weights. Finally, and perhaps most important of all, he should come to see in chemical stoichiometry one representative example of some of the most impressive constructions made by science. This is a construction built not by conjuring techniques or a passive faith but, rather, by the actively systematic coordination of experimental evidence and theoretical inference. As facts and theories become intimately joined and interlocked, in this construction, they begin to function as strong supports one of the other—and thus produce in the entire construction that remarkable combination of rigidity and flexibility that G. N. Lewis correctly regarded as archetypical of science (and scientists).

> The scientist is a practical man and his are practical [i.e., practically attainable] aims. He does not seek the *ultimate* but the *proximate*. He does not speak of the last analysis but rather of the next approximation. His are not those beautiful structures so delicately designed that a single flaw may cause the collapse of the whole. The scientist builds slowly and with a gross but solid kind of masonry. If dissatisfied with any of his work, even if it be near the very foundations, he can replace that part without damage to the remainder. On the whole he is satisfied with his work, for while science may never be wholly right it certainly is never wholly wrong; and it seems to be improving from decade to decade.

I acknowledge with deep gratitude the many helpful suggestions made to me by Francis T. Bonner, William H. Eberhardt, William F. Kieffer, and Richard J. Kokes—all of whom were kind enough to read through a preliminary edition of this book. To Jerry A. Bell I am greatly indebted for his meticulous line-by-line critique of that edition. To the Misses Diane Collins and Jenni Rochow I owe thanks for their careful typing of the final manuscript; to Mrs. Stephanie Pfaff and to my wife I am grateful for energetic assistance with galley proofs; and to Wayne Flicker I am much obliged for his construction of the index and his assistance with page proofs. Exclusive title to any remaining errors or obscurities is claimed for himself by the author.

L. K. N.

Cambridge, Massachusetts
April 1966

ACKNOWLEDGMENTS

I have been teaching most of the material in this text, in one form or another, for some twenty years; no doubt I am indebted, in some unknown degree, to many of the texts I have read during that period. I will at least note explicitly that Linus Pauling's splendid *General Chemistry* first suggested several of the problems cited in the present text. I must also express my gratitude to the Yale University Press, for permission to reproduce in the Preface the quotation from pp. 6 and 7 of G. N. Lewis' *Anatomy of Science* (1926); to McGraw-Hill, for permission to use, as my Figs. 2–12 and 2–14, redrawings made from figures that appear on pp. 13 and 14 of G. Barrow's *Physical Chemistry* (1961); to John Wiley & Sons, for permission to use, as my Fig. 2–15, a redrawing of a figure that appears on p. 455 of D. Halliday and R. Resnick's *Physics* (combined edition, 1962); Fig. 3–6 is redrawn from the *American Journal of Physics* (**33**, 18, 1965); Fig. 4–15 from *Biophysical Principles of Structure and Function* by F. M. Snell *et al.* (Addison-Wesley, 1965); and Fig. 5–3 from G. W. Castellan's *Physical Chemistry* (Addison-Wesley, 1964).

Contents

CHAPTER 1

THE ATOMIC-MOLECULAR THEORY

From the dawn of Greek science to the present, it has been taken for granted that the apparently limitless variety of complex materials, presented to us in our experience of the world, is resolvable into (and explicable in terms of) a limited number of "elements." Of course, what we take to be elements differs sharply from what were elements for the Greeks. Indeed, if we accept Lavoisier's operational definition of an element as "the last term at which analysis arrives," it is clear that the roster of elements may well be a changing one—depending on the methods of "analysis" brought into play. The familiar methods of the chemist yield a list of some 100-odd "chemical elements." If we bring to bear more sophisticated methods of analysis, these elements are still further resolvable, into distinct isotopic species like hydrogen and deuterium ("heavy hydrogen"). Even these isotopes may be further resolved, by high-energy analysis, into electrons, nucleons, and so forth. The meaning we attach to the concept "element" thus becomes a function of the experimental operations with which we are concerned. As for the classical problems of chemistry, it is both entirely legitimate and enormously productive to regard the 100-odd chemical elements *as* elements, for they are truly the last terms at which the classical methods of chemical analysis *do* arrive.

From these elements we can, as is well known, build up a great variety of chemical *compounds:* substances remarkable both for the striking differences of their properties from those of the component elements and for the comparative invariance of the proportion in which each compound contains its component elements. Well over a million such compounds are now known, and thousands more (most of them containing the element carbon) are being prepared and characterized each year. And then, again confronting the bewilderingly limitless variety of materials found in nature, we may aspire to comprehend even them—by conceiving them as built up from the limited numbers of elements and compounds with which we are (or expect to become) thoroughly familiar, and which we feel we can understand. What form will that understanding assume?

1

The Laws of Chemical Combination

In science the search for theoretical understanding generally sets out from empirical observations. We begin then with four major empirical regularities ("laws") that chemists have long regarded as well established.

▶ **The conservation of mass.** *In any chemical reaction the mass of the products is equal to the mass of the reactants.*

This generalization was set up by Lavoisier as the keystone of chemical investigation. Does it need to be qualified in the light of more recent findings on the equivalence of mass and energy? From Einstein's special-relativity theory, we know that if energy ΔE is emitted by a reaction system, that system will suffer a loss of mass, Δm, given by the equation

$$\Delta E = (\Delta m)c^2,$$

where c is the velocity of light. Now, no known (or readily imaginable) chemical reaction releases much more than 10 kcal per gram of product formed. (As a standard of comparison, consider that the violent hydrogen-oxygen explosion liberates less than 4 kcal per gram of liquid water formed.) Converting 10 kcal to ergs, and expressing c as 3×10^{10} cm/sec, we calculate the corresponding Δm in grams:

$$10^4 \times 4.2 \times 10^7 = (\Delta m) \times (3 \times 10^{10})^2,$$
$$\Delta m \doteq 5 \times 10^{-10} \text{ gm.}$$

That is, a chemical reaction can at most produce a fractional change of mass of the order of 5/10,000,000,000—which is entirely undetectable empirically. If then we restrict Lavoisier's conservation law to *chemical* changes, it is exact far beyond the limit of our capacity to verify it.

▶ **The law of definite proportions.** *A given compound, wherever obtained and however prepared, contains its component elements in a fixed proportion by weight.*

This generalization was the fruit of the painstaking analytical work of Proust (ca. 1800). One may well wonder why Proust had to labor to establish a law that seems nothing more than a truth by definition—since we customarily *define* a compound as a substance that contains its component elements in a fixed proportion by weight. In fact, what Proust established was that one can find in nature a large group of substances remarkable for the fixity of their proportions. Thus, what the law of definite proportions signalizes is the empirical demonstration that such a class of substances

TABLE 1–1

Compound	Percentage of oxygen, by weight	Grams of oxygen combining with 1 gm nitrogen	Ratio of weights of oxygen combining with 1 gm nitrogen
Nitrous oxide	36.4	0.57	1
Nitric oxide	53.3	1.14	2
Nitrogen sesquioxide	63.4	1.71	3
Nitrogen tetroxide	69.6	2.28	4
Nitrogen pentoxide	74.1	2.85	5

exists. That the law is indeed something more than a trivial truth-by-definition is further indicated by the fact that, today, we have so broadened our concepts of "compounds" that we recognize as such some materials that do not contain their elements in fixed proportions (but more of this later; see p. 144).

▶ **The law of multiple proportions.** *When two elements combine to form more than one compound, the different weights of one element that combine with a fixed weight of the other element stand to each other in the ratio of small whole numbers.*

The meaning of this law is made plain in Table 1–1, which contains data for the nitrogen oxides: note that the percentages of oxygen, based on a fixed (100-unit) weight of the *compound*, do not show the simple relation that is brought out when we calculate instead the weights of oxygen combining with a fixed weight of nitrogen. Today we recognize that many organic compounds have a very high degree of complexity, and that in such cases we must make a rather liberal interpretation of the word "small," but fortunately the law of multiple proportions (proposed by John Dalton ca. 1805) was already well established long before men brought the law to bear on these more difficult cases.

The law of equivalent proportions. Unlike the last two laws, the law of equivalent proportions expresses a broad relationship that embraces the combining proportions of *all* the elements in *all* their compounds. This relationship emerges only when we consider the different elements in quantities reduced to some common standard of reference. The choice of reference standard is essentially arbitrary. Traditionally, 8 gm of oxygen has been chosen as standard, and the *equivalent weight* of an element has been defined as the number of grams of that element which combine with

TABLE 1–2

Compounds	Grams of indicated elements combining with each other to form the indicated compounds			
	Na	H	Cl	O
Sodium oxide	23.0			8.0
Water		1.0		8.0
Chlorine monoxide			35.5	8.0
Sodium hydride	23.0	1.0		
Sodium chloride	23.0		35.5	
Hydrogen chloride		1.0	35.5	
Sodium hydroxide	23.0	1.0		16.0
Sodium perchlorate	23.0		35.5	64.0

8 gm of oxygen.* In terms of this new concept we can state as follows the law of equivalent proportions first adumbrated by Richter about 1795:

▶ *When elements combine with each other, they do so in proportion to their equivalent weights, or small whole number multiples thereof.*

A few representative modern data, giving substance to this rather abstract statement, are displayed in Table 1–2. Observing that 23 and 1 are respectively the weights of sodium and hydrogen that combine separately with 8 gm of oxygen, consider how very remarkable, how unforeseeable *a priori*, is the further fact that when sodium and hydrogen react with each other, they do so in the proportion 23 to 1. Observing how the same numbers, or simple multiples thereof, *constantly* recur, we recognize that we are dealing with no chance concatenation of data.

The Atomic-Molecular Theory

Empirical generalizations like the above four fairly clamor for theoretical interpretation. Taking these generalizations as rigorously exact, we find that they are convincingly explained and united in the simple theory created by John Dalton at the beginning of the 19th century. Moreover, when we later come to recognize that these generalizations are *not* exact,

---

* Oxygen was chosen as the reference element because it forms stable compounds with the vast majority of the chemical elements; 8 was chosen as the reference number in order that the smallest equivalent weight found (that of hydrogen) should have the value 1. If an element forms no stable oxide, its equivalent weight can still be fixed by reference to the secondary standard constituted by some other element whose equivalent weight has been established by direct reference to oxygen. Thus the equivalent weight of an element forming no stable oxide may be taken as the weight of that element which combines with (or displaces) 1 gm of hydrogen, 35.5 gm of chlorine, etc.

our theory will not be shaken. Only slightly amended, it will prove quite competent to account for all of the observed deviations from the simple behavior expressed in the four laws of chemical combination. We begin, then, by constructing the simple theory that rationalizes the four laws, considered initially as mathematically exact. The postulates of the theory are as follows:

1. A chemical element is made up of very minute, discrete, indivisible particles, or atoms (Gr. *atomos*, indivisible, uncuttable), that persist, unchanged and indestructible, through all chemical change.

2. All atoms of a given element are alike in all respects, and most notably in mass,* while atoms of different elements are characterized by different masses.*

3. A chemical compound consists of molecules that are stable groupings of definite, comparatively very small, integral numbers of atoms of the component elements.

In terms of these three postulates we can at once give a straightforward interpretation of the four empirical laws we felt challenged to explain.

Conservation of mass. In the perspective of these postulates, chemical reaction represents no more than a reshuffling or regrouping of atoms that are themselves immutable. Hence the number and identity of the atoms present in a closed system is exactly the same before and after reaction takes place. Since each atom conserves the mass characteristic of its species, the mass of the system as a whole must remain constant. Lavoisier's generalization is thus an obvious consequence of our atomic theory. Indeed, this theory construes chemical change in terms very similar to those suggested by Democritus some 2500 years ago. That is, the permanence of the world is viewed as a reflection of the immutability of its constituent atoms; the incessantly shifting appearance of the world is viewed as a reflection of the constantly shifting relative juxtaposition of these atoms.

Definite proportions. Let us take water as a compound exemplifying the law of definite proportions. On the basis of our second postulate, each hydrogen atom has some one absolute mass (h) characteristic of its species; each oxygen atom has some one absolute mass (o) characteristic of *its* species. From our third postulate, each water molecule can be represented by the

---

* Given the presently known existence of isotopes, one might do better to write *average* mass or masses; but even then this postulate would still need further revision, as we will see (p. 165). Hence it seems preferable to state this postulate in its simplest possible (Daltonian) form.

formula H_xO_y with the definite assurance that the numbers x and y (representing respectively the numbers of hydrogen and oxygen atoms combined in the molecule) are small whole numbers. In that case, wherever and however water molecules are formed, they will contain hydrogen and oxygen in an invariant ratio ($= x\,\mathsf{h}/y\,\mathsf{o}$) by mass, or weight. Observe that the number (η) of water molecules in the specimen at hand is completely irrelevant. Whatever the value of η, it will still be the case that

$$\frac{\text{weight hydrogen present}}{\text{weight oxygen present}} = \frac{\eta x\,\mathsf{h}}{\eta y\,\mathsf{o}} = \frac{x\,\mathsf{h}}{y\,\mathsf{o}}.$$

Multiple proportions. Let us again take the nitrogen oxides as compounds exemplifying the law of multiple proportions. Let us symbolize by n the absolute mass of a single nitrogen atom, and by o the absolute mass of a single oxygen atom. By assigning some plausibly simple formulas to the nitrogen oxides, we find it easy to rationalize their conformity with the law of multiple proportions, as shown in Table 1–3. Observe that at least two equally plausible sets of formulas (columns 3 and 6) are equally concordant with the experimental findings: *multiple-proportion data do not permit unequivocal assignment of formulas to the compounds concerned.* On the other hand, however uncertain we may be about the actual formulas, we can be confident that experimental data will always be consistent with the law of multiple proportions. This confidence derives from our third postulate, which assures us that the numbers of constituent atoms entering into the formation of molecules are always *small whole* numbers. Imagine, for example, that any two nitrogen oxides, (i) and (ii), have respectively

TABLE 1–3

	Experiment		Theoretical interpretations					
	1	2	3	4	5	6	7	8
Compound	Grams oxygen per 1 gm nitrogen	Ratios of figures in column 1	Possible formula set A	Mass oxygen uniting with η nitrogen atoms	Ratios of figures in column 4	Possible formula set B	Mass oxygen uniting with η nitrogen atoms	Ratios of figures in column 7
Nitrous oxide	0.57	1	NO	$1\eta\mathsf{o}$	1	N_2O	$\frac{1}{2}\eta\mathsf{o}$	1
Nitric oxide	1.14	2	NO_2	$2\eta\mathsf{o}$	2	NO	$1\eta\mathsf{o}$	2
Nitrogen sesquioxide	1.71	3	NO_3	$3\eta\mathsf{o}$	3	N_2O_3	$\frac{3}{2}\eta\mathsf{o}$	3
Nitrogen tetroxide	2.28	4	NO_4	$4\eta\mathsf{o}$	4	NO_2	$2\eta\mathsf{o}$	4
Nitrogen pentoxide	2.85	5	NO_5	$5\eta\mathsf{o}$	5	N_2O_5	$\frac{5}{2}\eta\mathsf{o}$	5

the formulas N_wO_x and N_yO_z. Let η represent the (large) number of nitrogen atoms present in some fixed number of grams of nitrogen. Consider then the two weights of oxygen that combine with this weight of nitrogen to form compounds (i) and (ii). To form compound (i) we require $\eta x/w$ atoms of oxygen; to form compound (ii) we require $\eta z/y$ atoms of oxygen. The ratio of the weights of oxygen combined with the fixed weight of nitrogen in the two compounds will then be

$$\frac{\text{weight oxygen in (i)}}{\text{weight oxygen in (ii)}} = \frac{(\eta/w)x \, \text{o}}{(\eta/y)z \, \text{o}} = \frac{yx}{wz}.$$

But since w, x, y, and z are stipulated small whole numbers—and allowing for the possibility of cancellations—it is clear that the ratio yx/wz must also represent a ratio of (at least comparatively) small whole numbers.*

Equivalent proportions. We focus on two elements, say hydrogen and chlorine. Let **H** and **Cl** symbolize the equivalent weights of hydrogen and chlorine—defined as the numbers of grams of those two elements that separately combine with 8 gm of oxygen. We seek now to show that when hydrogen and chlorine combine with each other, they do so in the proportion **H/Cl** or some small-whole-number multiple (or fraction) thereof. Let us symbolize by η the number of atoms of oxygen in 8 gm of oxygen, by H_wO_x and Cl_yO_z the formulas of the compounds used in establishing the equivalent weights of hydrogen and chlorine respectively, and by H_uCl_v the formula of the chlorine-hydrogen compound in which we are interested. How many hydrogen atoms will combine with 8 gm of oxygen to form H_wO_x?

$$\text{Number of atoms of hydrogen} = \frac{\eta}{x} \, w.$$

This, then, is the number of atoms present in just **H** gm of hydrogen. We can now express the mass (**h**) of a single hydrogen atom, as the quotient:

$$\text{h} = \frac{\text{H}}{\eta w/x} = \frac{\text{H}x}{\eta w}.$$

An exactly analogous train of reasoning permits us to express the mass (**cl**) of a single chlorine atom, as follows:

$$\text{cl} = \frac{\text{Cl}}{\eta y/z} = \frac{\text{Cl}z}{\eta y}.$$

---

* As stated (see p. 3), the law of multiple proportions refers most obviously to compounds containing *only* two elements. However, nothing in that statement seems to exclude compounds in which the two elements of primary interest are united not only with each other but with another element or elements as well. [*Query:* Will the law of multiple proportions apply to such cases, e.g. to the elements sodium and oxygen in the compounds $NaHCO_3$ and Na_2SO_4?]

Regardless of how much of the chlorine-hydrogen compound we take for analysis, the *ratio* of the weights of hydrogen and chlorine present will be given as

$$\frac{\text{weight of hydrogen}}{\text{weight of chlorine}} = \frac{u(\mathsf{h})}{v(\mathsf{cl})}.$$

Substituting the derived expressions for h and cl, we find the proportion of hydrogen to chlorine, in their compound with each other, to be

$$\frac{\text{weight of hydrogen}}{\text{weight of chlorine}} = \frac{u}{v} \cdot \frac{\mathsf{H}x/\eta w}{\mathsf{Cl}z/\eta y} = \frac{\mathsf{H}}{\mathsf{Cl}} \cdot \frac{uxy}{vwz}.$$

But all the symbols u, v, w, x, y, and z represent small whole numbers. Hence the combining proportion of hydrogen and chlorine *will* stand in the ratio of the respective equivalent weights, or some small whole number multiple (or simple fraction) thereof. In the not uncommon event that uxy and vwz represent the same combination of numbers, the combining proportion will be just the ratio H/Cl.

Clearly, the postulates of the atomic theory convincingly correlate *and explain* the four empirical generalizations from which we set out.

Relative Atomic Weights

In the Daltonian theory, atomic mass is the prime characteristic distinguishing different species of atoms. We have repeatedly used small letter symbols to represent the *absolute* masses of individual atoms of different species, but of course these *absolute* masses cannot be determined by the methods of classical chemistry. Nor are they, indeed, of the slightest use to chemists pursuing classical problems. All we need for such problems are *relative* atomic weights, and even to establish these represents, we will find, a very considerable undertaking.

A scale of relative atomic weights is set up by defining all atomic weights relative to the atomic weight of some one element selected as a standard and arbitrarily *assigned* a convenient numerical value. Historically, relative atomic weight scales have been based on the atomic weight of hydrogen taken as 1, the atomic weight of oxygen taken as 16, and (most recently) the atomic weight of carbon taken as 12. To write the defining equation for a scale of relative atomic weights, we use the following symbols:

$S =$ the defined relative atomic weight of the standard or reference element,

$\mathsf{s} =$ the absolute mass of a single atom of the reference element,

$X =$ the unknown relative atomic weight of some other element of interest,

$\mathsf{x} =$ the absolute mass of a single atom of that element.

Our defining equation then reads

$$\frac{X}{S} = \frac{\mathsf{x}}{\mathsf{s}} \quad \text{or} \quad X = \frac{\mathsf{x}}{\mathsf{s}} S.$$

The whole virtue of a scale of relative atomic weights is that it can be based entirely on determinations of *ratios* like $\mathsf{x/s}$, and does not demand that we attack the far more difficult problem of determining x and s *individually*. Once that ratio *is* established, since we ourselves assign a numerical value to S, the above equation can at once be solved for X, the relative atomic weight of the element in question.* A concrete example should make the situation entirely clear.

Let us take carbon as our reference element, and let us assign to it an atomic weight of 12.0.† Suppose that we wish now to establish the relative atomic weight of oxygen. We find experimentally that when 0.100 gm of pure graphite is burned in pure oxygen, just 0.367 gm of carbon dioxide is formed. We *assume* (since we have as yet no way of *establishing*) that the formula of carbon dioxide is CO_2. Symbolizing by c and o, respectively, the absolute masses of single carbon and oxygen atoms, and by η the number of molecules present in 0.367 gm of carbon dioxide, we can write

grams of carbon present $= \eta \, \mathsf{c} = 0.100$,
grams of oxygen present $= 2\eta \, \mathsf{o} = 0.367 - 0.100 = 0.267$.

We eliminate the unknown magnitude η by combining these two equations as follows:

$$\frac{2\eta \, \mathsf{o}}{\eta \, \mathsf{c}} = \frac{0.267}{0.100},$$

whence we easily establish that the value of the ratio $\mathsf{o/c}$ is

$$\frac{\mathsf{o}}{\mathsf{c}} = \frac{1}{2} \cdot \frac{0.267}{0.100} = \frac{0.267}{0.200} = 1.33.$$

That is, within the accuracy of our data, the mass of an oxygen atom is $\frac{4}{3}$ that of a carbon atom. With this ratio in hand, and the relative atomic

---

* In the last two paragraphs, a more consistent use of the word mass would be possible were we to speak, as some teachers recommend, of relative atomic *masses* rather than relative atomic *weights*. However, since we are concerned only with *ratios*, the numerical values will remain exactly the same, regardless of our choice of terminology—and we have elected to retain the traditional term, relative atomic weight. For an illuminating discussion of the general terminological problem, see "The Weight of Mass" by H. L. Armstrong, *Am. J. Phys.* **33**, 832 (1965).
† More precisely, ordinary carbon is assigned an atomic weight of 12.01115. The reason underlying this apparently peculiar (though obviously *permissible*) choice of reference value is noted on p. 164.

weight of carbon fixed at 12 by definition, we see at once that the relative atomic weight of oxygen is 16.0. More methodically, if we symbolize by O and C the *relative* atomic weights of oxygen and carbon respectively, we can readily substitute values to solve the defining equation:

$$\frac{O}{C} = \frac{\mathsf{o}}{\mathsf{c}}; \quad O = 12\left(\frac{0.267}{0.200}\right) = 12\left(\frac{4}{3}\right) = 16.0.$$

There is *nothing* absolute about such a number. [Query: What would we have found for the atomic weight of oxygen had we chosen the reference value $C \equiv 100$?] Another point worth stressing is that there are no *units* of atomic weight. A relative atomic weight (obtained as the product of a pure number and a mass *ratio*) is a dimensionless magnitude. Scarcely less important is the observation that this entire determination of relative atomic weight is dependent on our *assumption* of the formula of carbon dioxide: had we assumed the formula CO, or C_2O_2, the relative atomic weight of oxygen would have come out to 32.0.

We are accustomed to establishing relative molecular weights by a suitable addition of the relative atomic weights of the component elements. However, we will soon find occasion to wish that we could define relative molecular weights by the equation

$$\frac{M}{S} = \frac{\mathsf{m}}{\mathsf{s}},$$

where M is the relative molecular weight of the compound at issue and m is the absolute mass of one of its molecules. Actually, these two modes of establishing relative molecular weights are entirely equivalent. Consider the case of a molecule formed from x atoms of element A and y atoms of element B. With $C \equiv 12$ as the standard of reference, we use our proposed definition of molecular weight to write

$$\frac{M}{C} = \frac{\mathsf{m}}{\mathsf{c}} \quad \text{or} \quad \mathsf{m} = \frac{M}{12}\,\mathsf{c}.$$

The relative atomic weights (symbolized A and B) of the two elements are also involved in very similar equations:

$$\frac{A}{C} = \frac{\mathsf{a}}{\mathsf{c}} \quad \text{or} \quad \mathsf{a} = \frac{A}{12}\,\mathsf{c},$$

$$\frac{B}{C} = \frac{\mathsf{b}}{\mathsf{c}} \quad \text{or} \quad \mathsf{b} = \frac{B}{12}\,\mathsf{c}.$$

But certainly absolute masses may be taken as additive—hence, necessarily, $\mathsf{m} = x\,\mathsf{a} + y\,\mathsf{b}$. Substituting in this simple equation the expressions already obtained for **m**, **a**, and **b**, we find:

$$\frac{M}{12}\, \mathbf{c} = x\, \frac{A}{12}\, \mathbf{c} + y\, \frac{B}{12}\, \mathbf{c}$$

or simply,

$$M = x\,A + y\,B.$$

But this is precisely the familiar equation expressing the additivity of relative atomic weights—now *derived* from a definition of relative molecular weight that exactly parallels our definition of relative atomic weight.

The above calculations are clumsy in their symbolology, and needlessly so since the complexity arises from our introduction of symbols for absolute masses that we neither know nor care about. A more convenient mode of calculation—turning on a new concept—will now be developed.

The Mole Concept

The simplest and best methods for the calculation of atomic weights, molecular formulas, compositions by weight, etc., are no more than variants of a single, very general method for chemical calculations. This method is a direct outgrowth of our definition of relative atomic and molecular weights. If, for standard of reference, we take 12 as the atomic weight of carbon, the defining equations are

$$\frac{X}{12} = \frac{\mathbf{x}}{\mathbf{c}} \qquad \text{and} \qquad \frac{M}{12} = \frac{\mathbf{m}}{\mathbf{c}},$$

where X is the *relative* atomic weight of any element the absolute mass of whose atom is **x**, and M the relative molecular weight of any compound the absolute mass of whose molecule is **m**.

We now introduce the important concept of the gram-atom:

▶ A gram-atom of an element is a mass in grams of that element numerically equal to its relative atomic weight as defined by the equation $X/12 = \mathbf{x}/\mathbf{c}$.

We can at once grasp the significance of this new concept by rearranging the equation that defines relative atomic weights:

$$\frac{X}{\mathbf{x}} = \frac{12}{\mathbf{c}}.$$

Suppose that we take a gram-atom of carbon (that is 12 gm) and a gram-atom of element X. Observing that **c** is the absolute mass, in grams, of a single atom of carbon, and noting that we are dealing with a total mass of 12 gm of carbon, we see that the quotient 12/**c** is simply the total number of atoms of carbon present in one gram-atom of carbon. But a similar train of reasoning leads to recognition that the quotient X/x is simply the total number of atoms of the element X present in one gram-atom of *that* element. And then the last equation tells us that

$$\left\{\begin{array}{l}\text{Total number of atoms of}\\ \text{element X present in a}\\ \text{gram-atom of element X}\end{array}\right\} = \left\{\begin{array}{l}\text{Total number of atoms}\\ \text{of carbon present in a}\\ \text{gram-atom of carbon}\end{array}\right\}.$$

Observing that X can represent *any* element, and recalling that things equal to the same thing $(12/\text{c})$ are equal to each other, we can easily see that the number of atoms present in one gram-atom of any element is *always* the same. For our present purpose the actual magnitude of this number is of absolutely no consequence but, as we shall determine in Chapter 5, it is 6×10^{23}.

A second related concept—that of the gram-molecule—is developed along exactly the same lines.

▶ One gram-molecule of a compound is a mass in grams of that compound numerically equal to its relative molecular weight as defined by the equation $M/12 = \text{m/c}$.

An extension of the argument just given, proceeding now by way of the equation

$$M/\text{m} = 12/\text{c},$$

leads to the conclusion that the number of molecules present in one gram-molecule of *any* compound will always be the same, and will be equal to the number of carbon atoms present in 12 gm of carbon. Thus we arrive at a general conclusion:

▶ *The number of atoms in one gram-atom of any element and the number of molecules in one gram-molecule of any compound are invariably the same.*

This simple but important conclusion can at once be put to good use. The mass of a single atom, even were it known accurately, is far too small a unit to be used conveniently in routine calculations. Gram-atoms (and gram-molecules) represent far more suitable units, which our definitions of these concepts permit us to represent as follows:

$$\begin{array}{l}\text{number of gram-atoms}\\ \text{of an element}\end{array} = \frac{\text{number of grams of element present}}{\text{relative atomic weight of element}},$$

$$\begin{array}{l}\text{number of gram-molecules}\\ \text{of a compound}\end{array} = \frac{\text{number of grams of compound present}}{\text{relative molecular weight of compound}}.$$

And now we come to the main point. In view of the italicized generalization just made, we can set up what will be our Major Operating Principle (hereafter called MOP).

▶ **Anything that can be said about the relative numbers of atoms and molecules present in a given system can also be said about the relative numbers of gram-atoms and gram-molecules present therein, and conversely.**

The basis for this principle is no more profound than that for a corresponding "principle" asserting that anything that can be said of relative numbers of eggs and oranges can also be said of relative numbers of *dozens* of eggs and oranges. The basis for *this* "principle" is simply the fact that a dozen of anything always contains 12 objects; the corresponding basis for the MOP is our demonstration that a gram-atom of any element or a gram-molecule of any compound always contains the same number of atoms or molecules, respectively.

The great utility of the MOP is that often—merely by looking at a chemical equation, or even a few of the formulas appearing in it—we can at once say something about the relative numbers of atoms and molecules involved. From this theoretical statement, about relative numbers of atoms and molecules, the MOP then permits us to pass easily—*via* equations in gram-atoms and gram-molecules—to empirically verifiable statements about grams of elements and compounds. The value of this possibility emerges in the following illustrative example.

Illustrative Example. Aluminum sulfate can be obtained from ferrous sulfide by the following series of reactions:

$$FeS + HCl \rightarrow H_2S + FeCl_2,$$
$$H_2S + O_2 \rightarrow SO_2 + H_2O,$$
$$SO_2 + O_2 \rightarrow SO_3,$$
$$SO_3 + H_2O \rightarrow H_2SO_4,$$
$$H_2SO_4 + Al(OH)_3 \rightarrow Al_2(SO_4)_3 + H_2O.$$

Calculate the maximum weight of $Al_2(SO_4)_3$ that can be obtained from 100 gm of FeS by this route, given that the "molecular weights" of $Al_2(SO_4)_3$ and FeS are 342 and 87.8, respectively.

Observe that we have not troubled even to balance the equations for the reactions concerned, as surely we would have to were we to make a step-by-step calculation. But a step-by-step calculation becomes wholly superfluous as soon as we observe that all of the sulfur that enters as FeS must leave as $Al_2(SO_4)_3$, so that the maximum quantity of the second will be determined by the amount of the first available. By looking at the formulas FeS and $Al_2(SO_4)_3$, we see that (since the former contains 1 sulfur atom and the latter 3) we will use three "molecules" of FeS for each "molecule" of $Al_2(SO_4)_3$ produced. We can then write

$$\text{number of molecules of } Al_2(SO_4)_3 \text{ produced} = \frac{1}{3} \times \text{number of molecules of FeS used.}$$

By the MOP, any statement that can be made about relative numbers of molecules can be made also with regard to relative numbers of gram-molecules. Hence

$$\text{number of gram-molecules of } Al_2(SO_4)_3 \text{ produced} = \frac{1}{3} \times \text{number of gram-molecules of FeS used.}$$

The only difficult part of the problem—of *any* such problem— is completed at this point. For now we need only make numerical substitutions on the basis of our definition of the gram-molecule. Given that we used 100 gm of FeS having a molecular weight of 87.8, we used 100/87.8 gram-molecules of that material. And if we obtain α gm of $Al_2(SO_4)_3$ having a molecular weight of 342, then $\alpha/342$ is the number of gram-molecules of that material produced. Substituting in the last equation, we have

$$\frac{\alpha}{342} = \frac{1}{3} \frac{100}{87.8}.$$

The rest is arithmetic, and yields $\alpha = 130$ gm.

Two possibilities of extending the concept of gram-molecules and gram-atoms are suggested by the foregoing problem.

First: Suppose that the problem had been stated in pounds (or tons). Would we then laboriously convert to grams, work the problem as above, and then convert back to pounds (or tons)? This would be a farcical procedure. A moment's reflection suggests that the derivation of the MOP can easily be extended to pound-atoms and pound-molecules (or ton-atoms and ton-molecules, etc.). That is, the same line of reasoning shows that the number of atoms in a pound-atom of any element and the number of molecules in a pound-molecule of any compound are invariably the same. That number will be equal to the number of carbon atoms present in 12 *pounds* of carbon, and will obviously differ from 6×10^{23} (which is the number of carbon atoms in 12 *grams* of carbon). We must then take care not to *mix* our units in any given calculation: that is, we must carry it through with gram-molecules, *or* pound-molecules, *or* etc. But, subject only to this restriction, the MOP can be generalized to apply to *any* units of weight. Thus the above illustrative example would be solved for the case of 100 pounds (or tons) of FeS without the change of a single figure.

Second: Note that in stating our illustrative problem, we put quotation marks around the words "molecular weight" when referring to FeS and $Al_2(SO_4)_3$, and we should have put such marks around all subsequent references to "molecules" and "gram-molecules" of these substances. In regard to ferrous sulfide for example, by way of chemical analysis we can at most learn that the ratio of iron to sulfur atoms in this compound is 1:1. The formula FeS is the *simplest* formula expressing this ratio, but other formulas like Fe_2S_2, Fe_3S_3, or $(FeS)_x$—where x is any integer—would be equally consistent with the empirical ratio. For convenience we choose to work with the simplest possible formula. But, since this need not at all represent the actual molecular formula, we cannot legitimately speak of a molecular weight or a gram-molecule of FeS. However, we can quite properly speak of its *formula weight;* that is, Fe $(=55.8)$ + S $(=32)$ = formula weight of FeS $(=87.8)$. If we then create the concept of a *gram-formula,* it is plain that there will be as many formula-units of any compound present in a gram-formula of that compound as there are atoms in a gram-atom of any element. That is, if we take 87.8 grams of ferrous sulfide, we may be sure that we have as many FeS units as there are atoms of carbon in 12 gm of carbon. Thus we extend the MOP to statements in terms of gram-formulas. In the foregoing illustrative problem for example, we could, and should, have avoided the wholly unwarranted and entirely superfluous assumption that molecular formulas are known. The entire problem would then have been worked *not* in terms of gram-molecules but in terms of gram-formulas, and *neither the reasoning, the numbers, nor the answer would then differ in the slightest from the solution we have given.*

We have found that the MOP can be expressed in terms of the gram-atom, the gram-molecule, and/or the gram-formula. For convenience we often use a single word, the *mole*, to refer to all these concepts collectively. We then speak of a mole of Na, or H_2O, or FeS. However, one precaution is then essential. When one speaks of moles of Q (or gram-formulas of Q), one must always take care to insert for Q the appropriate chemical symbol, and *not* merely a name. To say one gram-atom of oxygen is unequivocally to signify 16 gm of oxygen; to say one gram-molecule of oxygen is unequivocally to signify 32 gm of oxygen; but to say one mole of oxygen is to leave in doubt whether one means 16 or 32 gm. Yet no ambiguity arises from the multiple reference of the word mole, *provided that* the particular atom or group of atoms in question is clearly specified—as when we say a "mole of O" or, as the case may be, a "mole of O_2." A mole of any specified species is simply the quantity that contains as many units of that species as there are atoms of carbon in 12 gm of carbon. Note that, ordinarily, the unqualified word mole refers to *gram* units: if other units are to be used, they must be indicated by explicit qualifications, as in pound-mole, ton-mole, etc.

Application to solutions. With the mole concept in hand, we turn to work with solutions. If we dissolve 1 mole of material in sufficient solvent to make 1 liter of solution, we say that the resulting solution is 1 molar (conveniently abbreviated 1 M). It is generally far quicker to measure out a volume of a solution than to measure out a weight of a solid and, if we know the molarity of the solution, there is no uncertainty about the number of moles of dissolved solid so dispensed. Thus 100 ml (i.e. one-tenth of a liter) of a 1 M solution will contain 0.1 mole of dissolved material. More generally, if we measure out V ml of solution having a molar concentration M, the number of moles of dissolved material so obtained is $MV/1000$, where the fraction $V/1000$ simply represents that fraction of 1 liter we have used. A broadly useful equation is obtained by considering that when V_1 ml of a solution with concentration M_1 is diluted with pure solvent to a final volume V_2, the total number of moles of dissolved material remains constant. Thus we can write

$$\frac{V_1}{1000} M_1 = \frac{V_2}{1000} M_2,$$

where M_2 represents the molarity of the diluted solution. We have then

$$V_1 M_1 = V_2 M_2,$$

which offers an easy way of calculating M_2 or, alternatively, an easy way of calculating how we should dilute a solution of some given molarity in order to obtain a solution with some other desired molarity.*

A slight extension of the same argument permits an important generalization of the utility of the above equation. Suppose that we wish to determine the unknown concentration of a NaCl solution by titration with a $AgNO_3$ solution of known concentration. From the stoichiometric equation,

$$NaCl + AgNO_3 \rightarrow AgCl \downarrow + NaNO_3,$$

we see that one $AgNO_3$ formula-unit must be added for each NaCl formula-unit present. Hence we can write

number of moles of $AgNO_3$ added = number of moles of NaCl present.

Representing by M_{AgNO_3} the known molarity of the $AgNO_3$ solution, and by M_{NaCl} the unknown molarity of the NaCl solution, we can then write

$$M_{NaCl} \frac{V_{NaCl}}{1000} = M_{AgNO_3} \frac{V_{AgNO_3}}{1000},$$

$$M_{NaCl} V_{NaCl} = M_{AgNO_3} V_{AgNO_3}.$$

Since M_{NaCl} represents the moles of NaCl per liter, it follows (by definition) that

$$\frac{\text{grams NaCl/liter}}{\text{formula weight NaCl}} \cdot V_{NaCl} = M_{AgNO_3} V_{AgNO_3}$$

or

$$\text{grams NaCl/liter} = \left(M_{AgNO_3} \frac{V_{AgNO_3}}{V_{NaCl}} \right) \text{formula weight NaCl},$$

---

* When speaking of a solution containing, say, 1 mole of $AgNO_3$, some texts designate the solution as $1F$ rather than $1M$, thus signifying that the solution contains 1 gram-formula of $AgNO_3$ and shunning any implication that dissolved silver nitrate has the molecular formula $AgNO_3$. However, given the general significance we have assigned the word mole, this refinement is superfluous. The designation "1 M $AgNO_3$" refers specifically to the formula-unit $AgNO_3$, whether or not that grouping represents a true molecular formula in either the pure solid or its solution.

whence it is clear that, by measuring the volumes of the two solutions used, we can determine the concentration of the NaCl solution. [*Query:* Suppose that, instead of a NaCl solution, we were concerned with a $BaCl_2$ solution, and wished to calculate M_{BaCl_2}. How would our calculation be changed?]

The Not-So-Eternal Triangle

Having in hand the facile mode of calculation that the mole concept makes possible, we return now to considerations of principle. We saw earlier that, given the *combining weights* in which carbon and oxygen unite with each other, and the *formula* of the compound so produced, we could easily calculate the *atomic weight* of oxygen relative to $C \equiv 12$. We wish now to examine the general relation of the three italicized parameters. They are so related that if any two are known, the third is at once calculable.

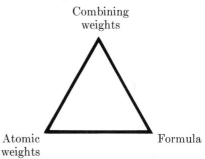

Combining (or reacting) weights from atomic weights and formulas.
Given that 1.01, 16.00, and 55.85 are the atomic weights of hydrogen, oxygen, and iron, respectively, calculate: (i) how many grams of metallic iron will be obtained when gaseous hydrogen (H_2) is used to reduce 15.97 gm of ferric oxide (Fe_2O_3), and (ii) how many grams of hydrogen will be used up in the reduction?

We know the weight of Fe_2O_3 present; we seek to relate this to the weight of iron produced. Here, as in many other cases, we can construct the connecting link (a molar balance) without even writing the balanced equation for the reaction involved. The only source of metallic iron is the Fe_2O_3. Looking at the formula Fe_2O_3, we see that each Fe_2O_3 unit contains two Fe atoms. That is,

$$Fe_2O_3 \rightarrow 2Fe.$$

The number of atoms of Fe formed is thus twice the number of Fe_2O_3 units used. Therefore

2 · number of Fe_2O_3 units used = number of iron atoms produced.*

---

* Notice how the number 2 has shifted in the last two expressions of the *same* relation. However, only the second expression is a genuine equation, for in the first the arrow signifies *not* an equality but, rather, the word "yields." In much the same way, 1 dozen eggs ⌐ yields ⌐► 12 eggs, and this fact is expressed algebraically by writing: 12 × number of dozen eggs = number of eggs.

We can now use the MOP to write

$$2 \cdot \frac{\text{number of gram-formulas}}{\text{of Fe}_2\text{O}_3 \text{ used}} = \frac{\text{number of gram-atoms}}{\text{of Fe produced}}$$

or, more concisely,

$$2 \cdot \text{moles of Fe}_2\text{O}_3 = \text{moles of Fe}.$$

The "difficult" part of the first answer is now completed: all that remains is to substitute numerical values in accordance with our definition of the mole concept. Given the atomic weights of iron and oxygen, we readily determine the formula weight of Fe_2O_3 as $[2(55.85) + 3(16.00)] = 159.7$. We are given also that the weight of Fe_2O_3 used is 15.97 gm. Hence

$$\text{moles of Fe}_2\text{O}_3 = \frac{\text{grams of Fe}_2\text{O}_3}{\text{formula weight Fe}_2\text{O}_3} = \frac{15.97}{159.7} = 0.1000.$$

Letting x represent the number of grams of metallic iron formed, we have

$$\text{moles of Fe} = \frac{\text{grams of Fe}}{\text{atomic weight Fe}} = \frac{x}{55.85}.$$

Substituting the last two equalities in the equation preceding them, we find that

$$2(0.1000) = \frac{x}{55.85},$$

whence $x = 11.17$ gm of metallic iron produced.

Turning now to part (ii), we observe that hydrogen is used up only in removing oxygen from Fe_2O_3. For each Fe_2O_3 unit introduced there are three oxygen atoms to be removed as H_2O and, thus, three H_2 molecules will be used up in the removal. This verbal statement can be given in an algebraic expression as follows:

$$3 \cdot \text{number of Fe}_2\text{O}_3 \text{ units used} = \text{number of H}_2 \text{ molecules required.*}$$

We now deploy the MOP to write

$$3 \cdot \text{moles Fe}_2\text{O}_3 = \text{moles of H}_2.$$

---

* Our original verbal statement might be "confirmed" by writing the "chemical equation" $Fe_2O_3 + 3 H_2 \rightarrow 2 Fe + 3 H_2O$. The writing of such an equation assures us that we did not forget anything in formulating the verbal statement, but the reasoning underlying the "equation" is identical with that underlying the verbal statement. Observe again the relocation of the coefficient 3 as between the "chemical equation" and the corresponding algebraic equation.

The number of moles of Fe_2O_3 used has already been found to be 0.100. Letting y represent the number of grams of H_2 required, the moles of H_2 required will be $y/(2 \cdot 1.01) = y/2.02$. On substitution, we then find that

$$3(0.100) = y/2.02,$$

whence $y = 0.606$ gm.

The practiced chemist will do such a problem in his head, and the reasoning so laboriously spelled out above will then be carried out almost subconsciously. But the reasoning here displayed in a very simple context is exactly the same kind of reasoning needed to solve the more formidable problems we shall encounter later. Such reasoning always involves the forging of some link (i.e. the writing of some equation) to connect what is known with what is sought. Having written an equation in terms of atoms, molecules, formula units, etc., we then use the MOP to rewrite it in terms of moles—and proceed thence to the calculation of combining or reacting weights in grams (or pounds, tons, etc.).

Atomic weights from combining weights and formulas. Quantitative oxidation of 1.000 gm of metallic titanium yields 1.668 gm of titanium dioxide, TiO_2. Taking the atomic weight of oxygen as 16.00, calculate the atomic weight of titanium.

The data indicate that in forming TiO_2, just 0.668 gm of oxygen reacts with 1.000 gm of titanium. The formula TiO_2 indicates that two atoms of oxygen are present for each atom of titanium present. Hence we write

$$2 \cdot \text{number of Ti atoms present} = \text{number of O atoms present},$$

whence it follows by the MOP that

$$2 \cdot \text{moles Ti} = \text{moles O}.$$

Representing by z the atomic weight of titanium, we find on substitution that

$$2\,\frac{1.000}{z} = \frac{0.668}{16.00}, \qquad z = \frac{32.00}{0.668} = 47.9.$$

Empirical formulas from combining weights and atomic weights. When 1.000 gm of a certain tin oxide is strongly heated under reducing conditions, 0.788 gm of metallic tin is produced. Given that the atomic weights of oxygen and tin are 16.00 and 188.7, respectively, determine the formula of the tin oxide.

Let us pause a moment to consider what will be our plan of attack on this problem. We are given not only the relevant atomic weights but also a pair of combining weights: 0.788 gm of tin combines with 0.212

(=1.000 − 0.788) gm of oxygen. How shall we use these data? Recall that the MOP concludes with the words ". . . and conversely." That is, anything we can say about relative numbers of gram-atoms we can say also about relative numbers of atoms. We are obviously in a good position to calculate the numbers of gram-atoms of the two elements present and, from these, the relative numbers of gram-atoms present. But, according to the MOP, these must also represent the relative numbers of atoms present—which is just what we need to establish the formula demanded. Let us then proceed with this plan:

$$\begin{array}{l}\text{number of gram-atoms} \\ \text{of Sn present}\end{array} = \frac{\text{grams Sn present}}{\text{atomic weight Sn}} = \frac{0.788}{118.7} = 0.00664,$$

$$\begin{array}{l}\text{number of gram-atoms} \\ \text{of oxygen present}\end{array} = \frac{\text{grams O present}}{\text{atomic weight O}} = \frac{0.212}{16.00} = 0.0133.$$

The absolute values of these numbers are clearly without any fundamental significance: they are dependent on our own arbitrary choice of a 1.000-gm sample for analysis. On the other hand, the *ratio* of these numbers should be entirely independent of our choice of sample size, and distinctively characteristic of the compound at issue. Dividing the second equation by the first, we find that

$$\frac{\text{number of gram-atoms oxygen}}{\text{number of gram-atoms tin}} = \frac{0.0133}{0.00664} = \frac{2}{1}.$$

within the accuracy of the data given.

And now, applying the MOP, we conclude that

$$\frac{\text{number of atoms of oxygen}}{\text{number of atoms of tin}} = \frac{2}{1}.$$

In our compound the number of atoms of oxygen is thus twice as great as the number of atoms of tin or, alternatively, there are 2 oxygen atoms for each 1 atom of tin present. Observe that we know nothing about absolute numbers of atoms present. We have only a *ratio* of numbers, or *relative* numbers.

The formula SnO_2 is the *simplest* formula consistent with our data, but other formulas, like Sn_2O_4, Sn_3O_6, etc., are equally consistent with the 2:1 ratio, which is all we can draw from our data. Thus, aside from our subjective preference for simplicity, we have *no* basis for choosing a *molecular* formula from among the limitless possibilities. We can, however, perfectly well make an objective assignment of the so-called *empirical* formula, which is, by definition, just the simplest formula consistent with the given data. In the present case the empirical formula is SnO_2 and, to mark it explicitly *as* an empirical formula, we may prefer to write it $(SnO_2)_x$. Here x is a number which must be integral—to avoid a fractionalization of atoms forbidden by the atomic theory—but which is otherwise unknown to us. In Chapter 4 we will consider how, given other data and principles, a particular value can often be assigned to a multiplier like x, in which cases unique molecular formulas can be assigned. However, we shall find also that in many cases (including that of SnO_2) there is good reason to doubt that a molecular formula even *exists*, in which event an empirical formula like that we have just established will be the *only* formula meaningfully assignable.

The unresolved problem. We have successfully completed our circumnavigation of the triangular array. We have examined three apparently distinct types of calculation, but it is now easy to show that they are in fact all based on a single equation. Consider that we have to deal with the compound $\mathcal{C}_a\mathcal{B}_b$. Let us represent by A and B the respective atomic weights of the two elements involved, and by α and β the weights in which they combine to form the compound. Suppose that some unknown number (η) of molecules of the compound is thus formed. We have ηa atoms of $\mathcal{C}$ combined with ηb atoms of $\mathcal{B}$, so that

$$\frac{\text{number of atoms of } \mathcal{C} \text{ present}}{\text{number of atoms of } \mathcal{B} \text{ present}} = \frac{\eta a}{\eta b} = \frac{a}{b}$$

or

$$\text{number of atoms of } \mathcal{C} \text{ present} = \frac{a}{b} \cdot \text{number of atoms of } \mathcal{B} \text{ present}.$$

But then we can use the MOP to write

$$\begin{array}{c}\text{number of gram-atoms}\\ \text{of } \mathcal{C} \text{ present}\end{array} = \frac{a}{b} \cdot \begin{array}{c}\text{number of gram-atoms}\\ \text{of } \mathcal{B} \text{ present}.\end{array}$$

If we have used α grams of $\mathcal{C}$ in forming the compound, the number of gram-atoms of $\mathcal{C}$ present is α/A and, following the same line of reasoning, the number of gram-atoms of $\mathcal{B}$ present is β/B. Substituting these expressions in the last equation, we obtain

$$\frac{\alpha}{A} = \frac{a}{b}\frac{\beta}{B}$$

or, more symmetrically,

$$\frac{\alpha}{\beta} = \frac{a}{b}\frac{A}{B}.$$

Given values for any two of the three ratios, this equation will permit us to calculate the third. The three types of problem we have discussed simply represent calculations in which different pairs of ratios have been assumed known. Observe that all we ever get from such calculations are *ratios*—

either the ratio of combining weights (or, equivalently, the weight of one element that combines with a stated weight of another element); or the ratio of atomic weights (which can be converted to the relative atomic weight of some one element by reference, through one or several ratios, to the atomic weight of carbon taken as 12.0); or the ratio of *a* to *b* (which we express as an empirical formula). This seems to be a very satisfactory wrap-up of the substantial powers of calculation we have drawn from the atomic theory.

Yet the position so far attained with the atomic theory still leaves a *great* deal to be desired. Our atomic theory hinges on the idea of atoms with distinctive weights and atomic groupings (molecules) with distinctive formulas. Are we in any position to establish these weights and formulas? *We are not!* Of the three ratios figuring in our summary equation, only *one* can be directly fixed by experiment. Combining weights *can* be established empirically, whether by synthesis or analysis of the compound in question. But beyond this we cannot go. Even after we have combining weights, to calculate an atomic weight we need at least an empirical formula, and to calculate even an empirical formula we need atomic weights. Always we need *two* of the three parameters in order to calculate the third and, alas, we know but one. We can give real substance to our atomic theory only by finding some other means of breaking into the refractory triangular array. Once we have made that break, the means of calculation we have considered will become thoroughly practicable and highly important. But, to achieve such a breakthrough, we must discover some *additional* line of approach, permitting us to establish either the atomic weights or the empirical formula when *neither* of these can be assumed known *a priori*. One obvious possibility has not so far been mentioned.

Gay-Lussac's Law and Avogadro's Hypothesis

A striking empirical regularity, discovered by Gay-Lussac in the first decade of the 19th century, may be expressed as follows:

▶ *In chemical reactions involving gaseous reactants and/or products, the volumes of the individual gaseous components (measured at constant temperature and pressure) stand to each other in the ratio of small whole numbers.*

In the electrolysis of water, for example, we find a 2 : 1 ratio in the volumes of hydrogen and oxygen released. If we run the reverse reaction (i.e. the hydrogen-oxygen explosion) at some constant temperature high enough to prevent condensation of the water formed, we find that the volumes of the reactants *and* product are all simply related, as follows:

2 volumes hydrogen + 1 volume oxygen → 2 volumes water vapor.

The unit of volume may be a liter, a milliliter, a cubic yard, etc. Since we are concerned only with the volume *ratios*, it makes no difference what unit of volume we use, provided only that we use it consistently.

The hydrogen-oxygen case is, of course, not an isolated instance. Small-whole-number ratios are found in a *great* variety of other reactions. For example,

1 volume hydrogen $+$ 1 volume chlorine $\rightarrow$ 2 volumes hydrogen chloride.

That the volume coefficients in each such reaction should stand in the ratio of small whole numbers is a quite unforeseen empirical finding. The combining *weights* in a given reaction manifest no such simple ratios; simple ratios emerge from combining-weight data only when we compare the values in *different* reactions, as in the laws of multiple and equivalent proportions. But no such manipulation is required when we deal with combining *volumes;* in any one given reaction *they* stand in the ratio of small whole numbers. How shall we seek to explain the law of combining volumes in atomistic terms?

When we find that the weight of oxygen combined with a given weight of carbon in carbon dioxide is twice as great as the weight of oxygen combined with the same weight of carbon in carbon monoxide, we are inclined to think that the formulas of carbon monoxide and carbon dioxide are respectively, say, CO and CO_2—rather than, say, $C_{123}O_{456}$ and $C_{123}O_{912}$. The first pair of formulas provides a convincing explanation of the observed weight ratio, since we readily understand how the postulated formulas might occur. The second pair of formulas does *not* provide an acceptable explanation of the observed weight ratio, since the postulated formulas are themselves even more remarkable than the data they are designed to explain. Consider, moreover, that the first pair of formulas (involving only small whole numbers) is entirely consistent with the law of equivalent proportions while, unless we are prepared to credit some miraculous coincidences, the second pair of formulas is inconsistent with the data expressed in that law. (Why?) Taking the laws of multiple and equivalent proportions *together*, we may then read their message thus: when elements combine to form compounds, the molecules of the latter are constituted from comparatively small numbers of atoms of the former.

We have now to consider the mutual relevance of two points:

1. When, under conditions of constant temperature and pressure, gaseous elements unite to form gaseous compounds, the *volumes* of the reactant elements and the product compound stand to each other in the ratio of small whole numbers. (This is an expression of direct observations, generalized as the law of combining volumes, and subject only to the constant-temperature-and-pressure restriction we hereafter symbolize with CTP.)

2. When the elements unite to form compounds, the *numbers* of the atoms of the reactant elements and of the molecules of the product compound stand to each other in the ratio of small whole numbers. (An inference drawn from the laws of multiple and equivalent proportions, this view is already implicit in Postulate 3 of our atomic-molecular theory.)

From these two propositions, one may draw [*Query:* How?] the following apparently straightforward conclusion:

Under CTP conditions the *numbers* of particles (i.e. atoms or molecules) present in *equal volumes* of gaseous elements and compounds stand to each other in the ratio of small whole numbers.

Given this conclusion, we readily understand how the strikingly simple behavior expressed in the law of combining volumes may be explained in atomistic terms. (How?) But the last proposition is not itself sufficient to offer us what we seek: an independent method for obtaining relative atomic weights of elements and/or the formulas of their compounds. The difficulty is that we know nothing about the identities of the small whole numbers that figure in the statement of that proposition. In 1811 Avogadro sought to deal with this difficulty by venturing the bold assumption that the small-whole-number ratios are all 1:1. That is, he proposed the following hypothesis:

Under CTP conditions the numbers of gaseous particles present in equal volumes of gaseous elements and compounds are invariably *equal*.

This proposition is clearly sufficient to supply, at least for gaseous elements, an independent method for the establishment of atomic weights. Suppose that (under CTP conditions) equal volumes of, say, gaseous hydrogen and gaseous oxygen *do* contain equal numbers of particles. Assuming these particles to be hydrogen atoms and oxygen atoms, respectively, we can at once determine the atomic weight of hydrogen, relative to that of oxygen, from readily accessible empirical data on the relative densities of these gases: i.e. the ratio of the weights of a standard volume of each gas measured under CTP conditions. Observing that the density of oxygen is 16 times that of hydrogen, we seem well justified in concluding that, relative to the atomic weight of oxygen taken as 16, the atomic weight of hydrogen is 1. Alternatively, or confirmatorily, we may proceed by way of the formula of water we can now deduce. If *two* volumes of gaseous hydrogen unite with *one* volume of oxygen to form water, then Avogadro's hypothesis implies that the formula of water must be H_2O. When this inference is put together with the known fact that, in combining to form water, hydrogen and oxygen unite in the weight ratio of 1 gm of hydrogen to 8 gm of oxygen, the MOP then lets us write:

$$\text{gram-atoms hydrogen} = 2 \cdot \text{gram-atoms oxygen},$$

$$\frac{1}{\text{atomic weight hydrogen}} = 2 \cdot \frac{8}{\text{atomic weight oxygen}},$$

whence it follows that

$$\frac{\text{atomic weight oxygen}}{\text{atomic weight hydrogen}} = \frac{16}{1}.$$

And so, using Avogadro's hypothesis, we draw from combining-weight and volume data a conclusion confirming that drawn, on the same hypothesis, from gas-density data alone. Thus, Avogadro's hypothesis does indeed seem to offer a promising line of attack on at least part of our problem. But, regrettably, that hypothesis is itself afflicted by very grave problems.

Observe that Avogadro's hypothesis is *not* a logical deduction *forced* on us by our data but only a plausible assumption apparently consistent with our data. That is, while it is permissible to hope that small whole-number ratios always take the simplest possible value, 1:1, it is not demonstrated that in fact they *do* have that value. And, actually, a closer scrutiny of the combining-volume data produces what seems a direct contradiction of the 1:1 assumption. We find experimentally that

2 volumes hydrogen + 1 volume oxygen → 2 volumes water vapor.

If we symbolize by η the number of gaseous particles in unit volume of each of these gases, Avogadro's hypothesis leads us to write

2η particles hydrogen + η particles oxygen → 2η particles water vapor

or

2 particles hydrogen + 1 particle oxygen → 2 particles water vapor.

Now each particle of water vapor must contain at least one atom of oxygen and, from the above equation, *two* particles of water vapor are formed for each *one* particle of gaseous oxygen used. This poses a nasty complication: the gaseous "particle" of oxygen cannot then consist of a single oxygen atom, as certainly seems most plausible *a priori*. Rather, that particle must be a molecule at least as complex as O_2 and, quite possibly, O_4, O_6, ..., depending on whether one water molecule contains 1, 2, 3, ... atoms of oxygen. We see no reason *a priori* why atoms of the same element should unite with each other, or why this union should then be terminated at some particular number like 2, 4, 6, ... And of course this incongruity is readily avoidable, by rejection of Avogadro's hypothesis. For then we could assume that there are only *half* as many molecules per unit volume of water vapor as there are oxygen atoms per unit volume of oxygen. In that case two volumes of water vapor will contain only as many water molecules as there are oxygen atoms per unit volume of oxygen. The last equation written above would then be rewritten as

2 particles hydrogen + 1 particle oxygen → 1 particle water vapor,

and there is *no* need to consider that the oxygen "particle" is anything different from a single oxygen atom.

The same situation arises in the reaction represented by the equation

1 volume hydrogen + 1 volume chlorine → 2 volumes hydrogen chloride.

If, on the one hand, Avogadro's hypothesis is sound, the gaseous particles of both hydrogen and chlorine must be more complex than single atoms. And if, on the other hand, the gaseous particles of all elements *are* single atoms (as we may well feel they should be), then Avogadro's hypothesis *cannot* be sound. In either case all is cast back into confusion. If we accept Avogadro's hypothesis, we must now deal with gaseous particles of the elements that are complex to a degree completely unknown to us, and possibly variable from one element to another. We cannot then draw from gas-density data secure conclusions about the relative atomic weights of the gaseous elements, nor can we infer the formulas of their compounds from combining volume data. (Why?) If, instead, we reject Avogadro's hypothesis (as most chemists did for half a century after its proposal), we have still to find what we desperately need: a method for establishing the relative atomic weights of elements and/or the formulas of their compounds. We seek a way out of this impasse in the next chapter.

Illustrative Examples

The following exercises, assuming availability of data we have yet to show accessible, are designed to consolidate your grasp of the concepts developed in the present chapter. In examining the illustrative examples, and in solving the succeeding problems, keep your attention focused on this central point: the effort to construct some bridge connecting what is *given* with what is *sought*. *All* problems demand some such construction. A systematic marshaling of the given data, and a consideration of how they may be related to what is sought, will usually suggest the connection through which the problem may be solved. In the case of problems in chemical arithmetic, the simplest and most trustworthy connection is invariably found in some sort of molar balance.

Illustrative Example. On strong heating, the oxygen is completely expelled from barium perchlorate, $Ba(ClO_4)_2$, leaving a residue of barium chloride, $BaCl_2$. From 3.36 gm of $Ba(ClO_4)_2$ there is obtained 2.08 gm of $BaCl_2$. When treated with excess aqueous silver nitrate solution, this $BaCl_2$ yields 2.87 gm of AgCl.

Given that the atomic weight of O is 16 and the atomic weight of Cl is 35.5, calculate

(a) the formula weight of $Ba(ClO_4)_2$, (b) the atomic weight of Ba,

(c) the formula weight of AgCl, (d) the atomic weight of Ag.

From one formula unit of $Ba(ClO_4)_2$ there are driven off 8 atoms of oxygen. Hence, by the MOP, one mole of $Ba(ClO_4)_2$ will yield 8 gram-atoms of oxygen, so that

$$\text{moles } Ba(ClO_4)_2 = \frac{1}{8} \times \text{ gram-atoms oxygen expelled}$$

$$= \frac{1}{8} \times \frac{\text{grams oxygen expelled}}{16}$$

$$= \frac{1}{8} \times \frac{3.36 - 2.08}{16} = \frac{1}{8} \times \frac{1.28}{16}$$

$$= 0.01.$$

Now

$$\frac{3.36}{\text{formula weight } Ba(ClO_4)_2} = \text{moles } Ba(ClO_4)_2 = 0.01,$$

in which case

$$\text{formula weight } Ba(ClO_4)_2 = \frac{3.36}{0.01} = \mathbf{336}, \qquad \text{(a)}$$

so that

atomic weight Ba $+$ 2 $\times$ atomic weight Cl $+$ 8 $\times$ atomic weight O

$$= \text{formula weight } Ba(ClO_4)_2$$
$$= 336,$$

atomic weight Ba $+$ 2 $\times$ 35.5 $+$ 8 $\times$ 16 $=$ 336,

atomic weight Ba $+$ 199 $=$ 336,

atomic weight Ba $=$ 336 $-$ 199 $=$ **137**. (b)

Observe that from each $Ba(ClO_4)_2$ formula-unit there is obtained one formula-unit of $BaCl_2$, and one formula-unit of $BaCl_2$ will yield two formula-units of AgCl. Therefore, by the MOP, from one mole of $Ba(ClO_4)_2$ there is obtained one mole of $BaCl_2$ and, thence, two moles of AgCl. But we have already calculated (see above) the number of moles of $Ba(ClO_4)_2$ present. There is 0.01 mole of $Ba(ClO_4)_2$. Hence we will obtain 0.01 mole $BaCl_2$ and 0.02 mole AgCl.

$$\text{moles AgCl} = 0.02,$$

$$\frac{\text{grams AgCl}}{\text{formula weight AgCl}} = 0.02,$$

$$\frac{2.87}{\text{formula weight AgCl}} = 0.02,$$

$$\text{formula weight AgCl} = \frac{2.87}{0.02} = \mathbf{143.5}. \qquad \text{(c)}$$

atomic weight Ag $+$ atomic weight Cl $=$ formula weight AgCl $=$ 143.5,

atomic weight Ag $+$ 35.5 $=$ 143.5,

atomic weight Ag $=$ 143.5 $-$ 35.5 $=$ **108**. (d)

Illustrative Example. When equal weights of mercury and iodine are brought together, the two elements react completely with each other. The product is a mixture of mercuric iodide (HgI_2) and mercurous iodide (Hg_2I_2). Set up a completely numerical expression from which the percentage of mercuric iodide in the mixture can be calculated. (Atomic weights: I, 127; Hg, 201. Formula weights: HgI_2, 455; Hg_2I_2, 656.)

The following is to be regarded as but one of several equally valid solutions for this problem. Let us first examine the possibility of setting up an equation. We know that the number of atoms of mercury originally present must be equal to the number of atoms of mercury present (in a combined state) in the product. Hence, by the MOP, there must be as many gram-atoms of mercury present at the end of the experiment as at its beginning. Our equation then runs

gram-atoms of mercury put in = gram-atoms of mercury in products.

More explicitly

gram-atoms Hg put in = gram-atoms Hg in HgI_2
+ gram-atoms Hg in Hg_2I_2.

We must now secure algebraic expressions to substitute for each of the terms in the last equation. Let us assume, for the sake of argument, that we start with 50 gm of mercury and 50 gm of iodine. Then, by the law of conservation of mass, the gross weights of HgI_2 and Hg_2I_2 must be 100 gm. Let us take x to symbolize the weight of HgI_2 present. Then $(100 - x)$ will be the weight of Hg_2I_2 present. To begin with we have 50 gm of mercury. Therefore

$$\text{gram-atoms of mercury originally present} = \frac{50}{201}.$$

Now consider the HgI_2 formed. For every formula-unit of HgI_2 present we have one atom of mercury. Hence, by the MOP, for every mole of HgI_2 present we must have one gram-atom of mercury. How many moles of HgI_2 are there? Plainly, there are $x/455$ moles of HgI_2. But this expression must also represent the number of gram-atoms of mercury combined in the HgI_2. Therefore

$$\text{gram-atoms of mercury combined in } HgI_2 = \frac{x}{455}.$$

And now, what about the mercury present in the Hg_2I_2? Looking at the formula, we see that each unit of Hg_2I_2 contains two atoms of mercury. Consequently, by the MOP, each mole of Hg_2I_2 must contain two gram-atoms of mercury. The number of gram-atoms of mercury in Hg_2I_2 must then be twice the number of moles of Hg_2I_2 present. We know that the number of moles of Hg_2I_2 present is $(100 - x)/656$. Hence

$$\text{gram-atoms of mercury combined in } Hg_2I_2 = \frac{(100 - x)}{656} \cdot 2.$$

Substituting the last three expressions in the second equation on the facing page, we arrive at the equation

$$\frac{50}{201} = \frac{x}{456} + 2\frac{(100 - x)}{656}.$$

This equation can be solved for x, the grams of HgI_2 in 100 gm of the mixture of mercurous and mercuric iodides, and thus the percentage of mercuric iodide present is established.

The student should convince himself (for example, by taking a as the original weight of mercury and a as the original weight of iodine) that the solution obtained is entirely independent of the original assumption that we are dealing with 50 gm of mercury and iodine. He ought also to convince himself that the problem is equally readily solved by forming an equation based on the conservation of the gram-atoms of iodine present rather than, as above, the gram-atoms of mercury.

PROBLEMS

1. On treatment with aqueous silver nitrate, 1.45 gm of holmium chloride ($HoCl_3$) yielded 2.30 gm of AgCl. Calculate the atomic weight of holmium. (Atomic weights: Cl, 35.5; Ag, 108.)

2. When radium bromide ($RaBr_2$) is heated in a stream of chlorine and hydrogen chloride, it is completely converted into radium chloride ($RaCl_2$). From 0.0130 gm of $RaBr_2$ just 0.0100 gm of $RaCl_2$ is obtained. Calculate the atomic weight of radium. (Atomic weights: Cl, 35.5; Br, 79.9.)

3. When 1.00 gm of metallic osmium reacts completely with chlorine (Cl_2), 1.75 gm of an osmium chloride is produced. Determine the formula of this chloride and write a balanced equation for the reaction. (Atomic weights: Cl, 35.5; Os, 190.)

4. On combustion with excess oxygen, a sample of a hydrocarbon (a substance containing nothing but hydrogen and carbon) yielded about 0.159 gm H_2O and 1.034 gm CO_2. Determine the empirical formula of the hydrocarbon. (Atomic weights: H, 1; C, 12; O, 16.)

5. When stannous fluoride, SnF_2, is treated with excess chlorine, the reaction that occurs may be represented by the equation

$$2SnF_2 + 2Cl_2 = SnCl_4 + SnF_4.$$

Calculate the number of pounds of stannic chloride that can be obtained by this process from 1 ton of stannous fluoride. (Atomic weights: F, 19; Cl, 35.5; Sn, 119.)

6. When the compound I_2O_5 is dissolved in water, it can be so treated that all of the iodine present is converted to iodide ion, I^-. When 3.34 gm of I_2O_5 is treated in this fashion, it is found that 2.16 gm of silver is required to precipi-

tate the iodide according to the equation $Ag^+ + I^- = AgI$. *This* reaction yields 4.70 gm of AgI. Relative to oxygen taken as 16

(a) what is the atomic weight of iodine;

(b) what is the atomic weight of silver?

7. When 1.2 moles of NaF are treated with excess $HClO_4$ and SiO_2, the fluoride is quantitatively converted to H_2SiF_6. The H_2SiF_6 is distilled and collected in a neutral $Th(NO_3)_4$ solution, forming insoluble $Th(SiF_6)_2$.

On the assumption that all reactions go to completion, determine:

(a) how many moles of H_2SiF_6 are formed;

(b) the equation of the precipitation reaction;

(c) how many grams of $Th(SiF_6)_2$ are obtained on filtration;

(d) how many moles of nitric acid, HNO_3, are present in the filtrate.

(Atomic weights: F, 19; Si, 28; Th, 232.)

8. When a mixture of NaBr and NaCl is repeatedly ignited with sulfuric acid, all the halogen material is expelled, and Na_2SO_4 is formed quantitatively. With a particular sample it is found that the weight of the Na_2SO_4 obtained is precisely the same as the weight of the mixture of NaCl and NaBr originally taken. Set up a completely numerical equation from which X, the percent by weight of the NaBr in the original mixture, can be computed. (Atomic weights: Na, 23; Cl, 35.5; Br, 79.9; S, 32; O, 16.)

9. In a laboratory experiment 414 gm of K_2CO_3 is treated with excess carbon and nitrogen in a high-temperature furnace. The reaction that occurs may be represented by the equation

$$K_2CO_3 + 4C + N_2 = 3CO + 2KCN.$$

The KCN so obtained is then carried successively through the reactions represented in the following equations:

$$6KCN + FeSO_4 = K_4Fe(CN)_6 + K_2SO_4,$$

$$2K_4Fe(CN)_6 + 3ZnSO_4 = K_2Zn_3[Fe(CN)_6]_2 + 3K_2SO_4.$$

On the assumption that all reactions go to completion, determine:

(a) how many ml of 0.5 M $ZnSO_4$ are required for the reaction represented in the last equation;

(b) how many grams of $K_2Zn_3[Fe(CN)_6]_2$ will be obtained.

(Formula weights: K_2CO_3, 138; $K_2Zn_3[Fe(CN)_6]_2$, 698.)

10. When treated with HNO_3, 6.334 gm of metallic Ag yields 9.976 gm of $AgNO_3$. In a second part of the experiment, just 1.000 gm of NH_3 was exactly neutralized with HBr, according to the equation $NH_3 + HBr = NH_4Br$. It was then found that the 9.976 gm of $AgNO_3$ formed in the first part of the experiment is just sufficient to react with all the NH_4Br, according to the equation $NH_4Br + AgNO_3 = AgBr + NH_4NO_3$. Taking the atomic weight of hydrogen as 1.008, set up two (simultaneous) equations from which the atomic weights of silver and nitrogen can be calculated (relative to oxygen taken as 16).

11. Two chlorides of a metal contain 49.09% and 53.63%, respectively, of chlorine.

   (a) Show that these compounds are in harmony with the law of multiple proportions.
   (b) What are the simplest formulas of the compounds, and what is the corresponding atomic weight of the element?
   (c) Considering the other possible formulas, what other atomic weights are possible?
   (d) What is the metal? (Refer to the table of atomic weights.)

   (Atomic weight: Cl, 35.5.)

12. The reaction $Zn + 2AgNO_3 = 2Ag + Zn(NO_3)_2$ goes essentially to completion to the right. Exactly 5.00 gm of metallic Zn was added to 100 ml of a silver nitrate solution. After all the silver in the solution had been deposited in metallic form, it was noted that not all the zinc had dissolved. The total weight of the excess (unreacted) zinc and the deposited silver was 7.00 gm. Calculate

   (a) the grams of silver deposited; and
   (b) the molarity of the silver nitrate solution.

   (Atomic weights: Zn, 65; Ag, 108.)

CHAPTER 2

THE KINETIC-MOLECULAR THEORY

From telescopic observations, one might plot routes for various expeditions on the surface of the moon, but the possibility of actually conducting any such expeditions remains remote (both literally and figuratively) until one has devised a space vehicle competent to reach the lunar surface. In our present inquiry we stand in a strikingly analogous position. In Chapter 1 we mapped out the connections between formulas, atomic weights, and combining (or reacting) weights; we have shown in detail how, given values for any two of these three parameters, we could calculate the third. But the possibility of actually carrying through any such calculation remains remote until we have devised some method sufficient to *determine* the parameter values we have until now simply *assumed*. Avogadro's hypothesis offers, we saw, a potential foundation for the method we need, *provided that* we can establish the solidity of that foundation hypothesis. To attain this goal, we begin by carrying through a general inquiry into the physical nature of the gases to which Avogadro's hypothesis refers. We will pursue the same progression followed in Chapter 1. That is, we begin with some generalizations expressing observable regularities in the behavior of the materials in question. Taking these to be rigorous (which they are not), we then seek to construct a set of theoretical postulates— which, in effect, propose a *model* for a gas—from which we can derive the observed regularities. These derivations prove sufficiently convincing to give us confidence in our theory, and we can then place Avogadro's hypothesis on a secure footing by *deriving* it also from that theory. In conclusion, we show how our first theory must be modified to explain the fact that the empirical laws with which we began are not quite rigorous, and we examine how these modifications affect the status of Avogadro's hypothesis.

The Gas Laws

▶ **Boyle's law.** *At constant temperature, a constant quantity* of gas exerts a pressure inversely proportional to its volume.*

Taking α to represent the proportionality constant, we can state the law algebraically, as $P = \alpha(1/V)$. This equation implies that under the indicated conditions, the product of pressure and volume will be constant, so that alternative expressions for the law are $PV = \alpha$ and $P_1V_1 = P_2V_2 = \cdots$. However expressed, this law offers a quantitative description of the strikingly extensive compressibility and expansibility of gases that Boyle called "the spring of the air." The kind of apparatus required to demonstrate Boyle's-law behavior is assumed familiar (see Fig. 2–1). The volume of the gas is read off from the graduations of the buret shown at the left. At equilibrium, the pressure of the gas must be equal to the pressure imposed on it—which is the sum of the hydrostatic head h_1 and the pressure exerted by the atmosphere on the exposed surface of mercury in the leveling bulb. The magnitude of the atmospheric pressure can be read from the barometer shown at the right: the height at which the mercury stands in the barometer is a measure of the pressure exerted by the atmosphere on the exposed surface of the mercury in the cistern at the base of the barometer. For the gas pressure (P) we can then write $P = h_1 + h_2$. If we agree to give h_1 a *negative* sign when the mercury in the leveling bulb stands *below* the mercury in the buret, this equation will offer a general expression permitting us to determine the pressure of a gas from two simple measurements of length. This pressure can be expressed directly as the number of millimeters (or centimeters, or inches, or . . .) representing the combined observed length of the two mercury columns. For, as is most evident if we write Boyle's law in the form $P_1/P_2 = V_2/V_1$, only the *ratios* of pressures and volumes matter—and these remain unchanged whatever units of pressure and volume we use, if only we use them consistently throughout any given calculation.

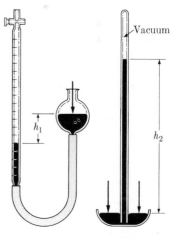

Figure 2–1

---

* For the moment, constant mass would be quite sufficient, but later (see p. 139) we will want to interpret "constant quantity" as "constant number of moles."

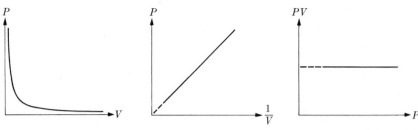

Figure 2–2

Three alternative graphical representations of Boyle's-law behavior are shown in Fig. 2–2. The rectangular hyperbola shown in the first graph well expresses the inverse proportionality of P and V (that is, $V \rightarrow 0$ as $P \rightarrow \infty$, and conversely). But such a curve does not readily lend itself to interpolations and extrapolations we often wish to make when, having available only a few experimental observations, we want to estimate the state of the gas under still other conditions. For this purpose the second graph offers a more advantageous representation of the inverse proportionality: the straight line, with slope equal to the proportionality constant α, readily permits both interpolation and extrapolation. The third and simplest graph is an obvious expression of the constancy of the PV-product at all pressures. Actual experimental data fall quite closely on the curves indicated above, *provided that* one confines oneself to measurements at reasonably low pressures.

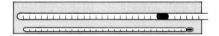

Figure 2–3

Charles' law. Under constant-pressure conditions, a constant quantity of gas shows a response to changes of temperature that is both much larger and much more uniform than that of solids or liquids. A simple apparatus yielding a quantitative measure of this response is shown in Fig. 2–3. A constant quantity of gas is confined by a mercury slug in a horizontal tube of uniform cross section, which is enclosed, with a thermometer, in a controlled-temperature region. Whenever the mercury slug is stationary, the internal pressure must be equal to the (approximately constant) external pressure exerted by the atmosphere. Systematically varying the temperature, we determine the gas volumes corresponding to each temperature. We find that our data can be well represented by the equation

$$\frac{V_1}{t_1 + 273} = \frac{V_2}{t_2 + 273} = \cdots = \beta,$$

where t represents the Celsius (i.e. centigrade) temperature read from the thermometer, β is a constant with value dependent on the quantity of gas taken for study, and the 273 is an empirical constant wholly independent of both the quantity and identity of the gas concerned. The temperature dependence of the volumes of liquids and solids is often expressible in an equation of similar form. But in such cases the empirical constant is much larger than 273, reflecting the fact that, under constant pressure, the volumes of liquids and solids do not change nearly so much with temperature as do the volumes of gases. And, much more important, the empirical constant is found to vary widely from one liquid or solid to another—which makes especially striking the fact that, for *all* gases at reasonably low pressures, this empirical constant is almost exactly the *same*.

One may take this notable regularity in the thermal behavior of gases as the foundation for a revised scale of temperatures. The familiar Celsius scale is determined entirely by the properties of a single substance (water) chosen arbitrarily from among a great many other possibilities which would have given other scales of temperature. The zero of temperature on this scale is fixed only as the melting point of ice, which, though

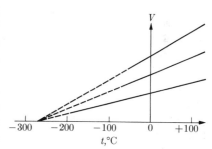

Figure 2–4

amply convenient, is completely arbitrary as a reference point. We may well hope to found a more significant reference zero on the behavior of the great *group* of gaseous substances. Accompanying Fig. 2–4 offers a graphical representation of the behavior expressed in the last equation. In each case the slope of the line (equal to the proportionality constant β) depends on what mass of which gas is taken for study, and on the magnitude of the constant pressure under which it is studied. Since all gases condense to liquids or solids at temperatures above −273°C, the distance over which we must extrapolate each line, at its low-temperature end, will be a function of the boiling point of the particular gas in question. However, these many differences notwithstanding, it is obvious from the form of the equation concerned that *all* these lines must converge identically toward an intercept of the horizontal axis at −273°C (more precisely, −273.15°C). This point offers a promising reference zero for the scale of temperatures we now define by the equation

$$T\ (°K) = t\ (°C) + 273.15,$$

where T represents *degrees absolute* or *degrees Kelvin*. The temperature *interval* of 1° remains the same on both scales: we still have a span of 100° between the melting point of ice (273.15°K) and the boiling point of water (373.15°K). The only difference is that the "absolute" scale has been based on the choice of a different reference point for 0°.

However more or less absolute this new scale may be, it is clearly a very *convenient* scale to use in work with gases. For now, instead of writing our empirical regularity as

$$\frac{V_1}{t_1 + 273} = \frac{V_2}{t_2 + 273},$$

we can represent it more compactly as

$$V_1/T_1 = V_2/T_2.$$

This equation expresses Charles' law, which can also be stated verbally as follows:

▶ *At any constant pressure, a constant quantity of gas occupies a volume directly proportional to the absolute temperature.*

Combined Form of Boyle's and Charles' Laws, and Amontons' Law

The constant-temperature restriction on Boyle's law and the constant-pressure restriction on Charles' law seriously limit the usefulness of these laws. Can we not obtain some more general law free from these restrictions? Indeed we can, but we must proceed with some circumspection in combining two equations that only hold subject to two *different* restrictions. Let us consider a quantity of gas occupying a volume V_1 at temperature T_1 and pressure P_1, and let us ask what volume (V_2) it will occupy at some different pressure (P_2) and temperature (T_2). An answer is easily obtained by employing the artifice of a two-step process. In the first step we use Boyle's law to calculate the volume (V^*) that the gas will occupy when the pressure is changed from P_1 to P_2 at *constant temperature* T_1. Knowing V^* for the conditions P_2 and T_1, we then use Charles' law to calculate the final volume V_2 attained when the temperature is changed from T_1 to T_2 at *constant pressure* P_2. Regarding volume as a function of the state of the system, we feel confident that the volume calculated for the two-step process cannot be different from that obtained when both P and T are changed simultaneously.

For the first step we write

$$P_1V_1 = P_2V^*$$

or

$$V^* = \frac{P_1}{P_2} V_1.$$

For the second step we write

$$\frac{V^*}{T_1} = \frac{V_2}{T_2}.$$

Eliminating V^* by substituting from the first equation into the second, we find that

$$V_2 = \frac{T_2}{T_1} \frac{P_1}{P_2} V_1,$$

which allows us to calculate the second volume from the first when *both* temperature and pressure are permitted to change. This general equation is not one to be memorized and applied blindly. All one need remember is that the final volume is obtained from the initial volume by multiplying the latter by a ratio of pressures and a ratio of temperatures (in °K). The detailed formation of the proper ratios is then, as shown in the illustrative example below, merely a matter of common sense.

The strong dependence of gas volume on temperature and pressure means that a statement of gas volume is meaningless unless accompanied by some specification of the pressure and temperature at which that volume was measured. To avoid all need for explicit statement of these essential qualifying conditions in each individual case, it is customary to report gas volumes for certain *standard* conditions of temperature and pressure, which by convention are taken as 0°C (273°K) and 1 atm pressure (760 mm mercury, 76 cm mercury). That is, instead of reporting a gas volume as actually *measured*, one reports the STP volume (i.e. volume under Standard Temperature and Pressure) calculated from the empirical observations.

Illustrative Example. You are about to purchase some rare and expensive gas. You are offered, at the same price, either 100 ml STP of the gas or 10,000 ml measured at 10 mm Hg pressure and 150°C. Which is the better buy?

A comparison becomes possible as soon as one reduces both volumes to the *same* conditions of temperature and pressure, and by convention one chooses STP conditions. Hence we will calculate the STP volume of the 10,000 ml measured at 10 mm Hg and 150°C (423°K). To obtain the STP volume we must multiply 10,000 by a pressure ratio and a temperature ratio. To reach STP conditions we must *increase* the pressure (from 10 to 760 mm) and to this change must correspond a *decrease* of volume; hence, the appropriate ratio is 10/760. Furthermore, to reach STP conditions, we must *decrease* the temperature (to 273°K), and, since this change must also *decrease* the volume, the appropriate ratio will be 273/423. We have then

$$V_{\text{STP}} = 10,000 \frac{10}{760} \frac{273}{423} = 85 \text{ ml.}$$

The first offering is therefore the better buy.

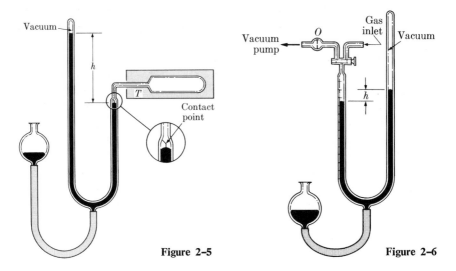

Figure 2–5   Figure 2–6

Another practically convenient expression of the combined gas law is

$$\frac{V_1}{V_2} \frac{P_1}{P_2} \frac{T_2}{T_1} = 1,$$

which shows that we can use any units of pressure and volume we like, provided only that we use them consistently throughout any one calculation. One last rearrangement yields

$$\frac{P_1 V_1}{T_1} = \frac{P_2 V_2}{T_2}.$$

Like all other forms of the combined gas law, this relation remains subject only to a constant-quantity restriction.* If now we further impose a *constant-volume* restriction, stipulating that $V_1 = V_2$, our last equation is reduced to

$$\frac{P_1}{T_1} = \frac{P_2}{T_2}.$$

This is Amontons' law—first established empirically but, as we have just seen, readily derivable from the combination of Boyle's and Charles' laws.

Amontons' law offers an expression well adapted to use in the determination of absolute temperatures. With the apparatus shown in Fig. 2–5, we can easily determine the ratio of two absolute temperatures reigning suc-

---

* We can make this restriction explicit by writing the last equation as $PV/T = \theta$, and noting that the magnitude of the constant θ varies with the mass of the particular gas sample under consideration.

cessively in the enclosure. We need only measure, at the two temperatures, the corresponding pressures of the enclosed gas sample, as indicated by the height-differential h. To ensure that all measurements are made at constant volume, we need only preface each pressure reading with whatever manipulation of the leveling bulb is necessary to bring the mercury in the right arm of the manometer to some fixed reference position, e.g. barely touching a rigid contact point. After making due correction for the (comparatively small) fraction of the total gas volume that stands outside the enclosure in which the temperature is controlled, we can then express the ratio of absolute temperatures as a ratio of measurable pressures, that is, $T_2/T_1 = P_2/P_1$. Once we have assigned a numerical value to any one particular temperature (for example, 273.15°K as the temperature of melting ice) we can in this way assign numerical values to all other temperatures.

▶ **Graham's law.** *Different gases held under the same (low) pressure effuse at rates inversely proportional to the square roots of their respective densities.*

The meaning of *effusion rate* can best be established by describing an experimental operation through which such a rate can be determined. Using the apparatus shown in Fig. 2–6, we charge the buret with a small amount of some gas A. By suitable manipulation of the leveling bulb, we adjust the gas pressure to some standard low value (say 1 mm) indicated by the height differential h, and throughout the experiment we continually adjust the bulb to hold h constant. We turn the stopcock to connect the buret with a fine hole, or orifice, in the membrane, shown at O. The other side of this membrane is maintained at high vacuum by continuous operation of a pump. The rate of flow of gas through the orifice is monitored by measuring the time interval (Δt_A) corresponding to some observable diminution (ΔV_A) of the volume of gas present in the buret. The rate of effusion (r_A) of the gas under these experimental conditions is then established by way of the equation $r_A = \Delta V_A/\Delta t_A$. Repeating the experiment with some other gas (B) held at the *same working pressure*, we similarly determine an effusion rate $r_B = \Delta V_B/\Delta t_B$. We are then in a position to state Graham's law algebraically as

$$r_B/r_A = \sqrt{\delta_A/\delta_B},$$

where δ_A and δ_B stand for the densities of the two gases, each measured under the same conditions of temperature and pressure that prevailed in the buret during the measurement of effusion rate.

At the very low working pressure the correspondingly minute individual gas densities may be hard to measure, but such measurements are actually wholly superfluous. For all that concerns us is the *ratio* of gas densities; and it is easy to show* that, other things being equal, the *ratio* of densities at the working pressure is the very same as the *ratio* of densities easily measured at some much higher pressure, for example 1 atm. From the fact that the densities of oxygen and hydrogen stand, respectively, in the ratio 16:1 at atmospheric pressure and room temperature, we can infer that 16:1 is also the ratio of the densities of these gases at room temperature and *any* other one pressure, for example 1 mm. Effusion measurements do indeed show that the rate for hydrogen is four times that for oxygen, as Graham's law requires, and similar measurements made on many other gases provide a strong empirical foundation for Graham's law.

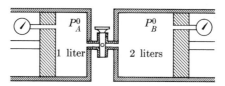

Figure 2-7

Dalton's law. "Every gas is as a vacuum to every other gas" is Dalton's vivid statement. That is, in a gaseous mixture each component exerts a "partial pressure" identical with that it would exert were it in sole occupancy of the volume in question. Consider the apparatus shown in Fig. 2-7, assuming that (1) the volumes of the connecting line and of the pressure gages are negligible compared with the indicated volumes swept out by

---

* Consider Boyle's law: $P_1V_1 = P_2V_2$, or $(V_1/V_2) = (P_2/P_1)$. Simply as a matter of definition, the density of a given parcel of gas must be inversely proportional to its volume. Thus it follows that for a given sample of gas at a given temperature, the ratio of the two densities observed at two different pressures will be

$$\delta_2/\delta_1 = P_2/P_1.$$

Let δ_A and δ_B represent the densities of gases A and B at the actual working pressure P, and let δ_A^* and δ_B^* represent the corresponding densities at some much higher pressure P^*. Applying the last equation to each of the gases separately, we find that

$$\delta_A/\delta_A^* = P/P^*$$

and

$$\delta_B/\delta_B^* = P/P^*,$$

which, on combination, yield

$$\delta_A/\delta_B = \delta_A^*/\delta_B^*, \qquad \text{Q.E.D.}$$

[*Query:* What is the *minimum* restriction on temperature(s) that must be satisfied if the last relation is to be applied?]

the pistons, (2) the temperature is maintained constant, and (3) only mixtures of gases that do not react with each other are to be taken into account.

Suppose first that we have the same gas present in both cylinders at 1-atm pressure. If we open the stopcock with both pistons locked in place then, since throughout the system we have the same gas at the same pressure, we should see *no* change of pressure. Suppose now that we have present two *different* gases: A on the left, B on the right. It is not then at all obvious what will happen when the stopcock is opened while the pistons are locked in place; even if the initial pressures P_A^0 and P_B^0 are equal, surely the gases will interdiffuse to form a homogeneous mixture. What will be the total pressure of that mixture? On Dalton's view, each gas exerts its own partial pressure independent of the presence of others. In that case we need only make a simple Boyle's-law computation for each component *separately*. Component A expands from 1 liter to 3 liters. Hence

$$p_A = \tfrac{1}{3}P_A^0,$$

where p_A represents the partial pressure of A in the mixture. The same line of reasoning applied to B gives

$$p_B = \tfrac{2}{3}P_B^0.$$

The total pressure (P_{AB}) can then be established as the sum of the partial pressures:

$$P_{AB} = p_A + p_B = \tfrac{1}{3}P_A^0 + \tfrac{2}{3}P_B^0 = 1 \text{ atm.}$$

if $P_A^0 = P_B^0 = 1$ atm.

Were P_A^0 and P_B^0 different from 1 atm, we could still calculate the final pressure from the above equation, and, in general, the results thus predicted on Dalton's law are excellently confirmed by experiment.

Suppose that we conduct the experiment differently. Starting with P_A^0 on the left and P_B^0 on the right, we lock the piston on the left and, as we open the stopcock, drive in the piston on the right to force all of gas B into the container on the left. What then is the final pressure? Observe that gas A still occupies its original volume so that, after the mixing process, $p_A = P_A^0$. But gas B has been compressed to half its original volume, so that $p_B = 2P_B^0$. Thus we have for the final mixture

$$P_{AB} = p_A + p_B = P_A^0 + 2P_B^0 = 3 \text{ atm.}$$

if $P_A^0 = P_B^0 = 1$ atm.

Were P_A^0 and P_B^0 different from 1 atm, we could still use this equation to calculate the final pressure, and, once again, Dalton's law gains strength from numerous empirical confirmations of such calculated values.

We can now give a more explicit statement of Dalton's law.

▶ *In mixtures of nonreacting gases, the total pressure is the sum of the partial pressures of the component gases.*

That is,

$$P_{\text{mixt}} = p_A + p_B + \cdots = \sum p_i,$$

where the partial pressure of each component is calculated simply as the pressure that component would exert if it were in sole occupancy of the entire volume in question. If constant-temperature conditions are maintained, if all components are at the same original pressure, and if the final pressure of the mixture is made equal to the original pressure of each component, we can speak also of an additivity of volumes, that is, $V_{\text{mixt}} = \sum v_i$. Thus, for example, we may regard air as a mixture in which the partial pressure of nitrogen is $\frac{4}{5}$ atm and the partial pressure of oxygen is $\frac{1}{5}$ atm; or, alternatively, as a mixture made up from $\frac{4}{5}$ volume of nitrogen and $\frac{1}{5}$ volume of oxygen, both initially at 1 atm pressure. The statement in terms of partial pressures is ordinarily the more useful.

Given Dalton's law, we note an important correction that must be made whenever, as is often the case, we collect and measure a gas over a volatile liquid (e.g. water). In the system indicated in Fig. 2–8, the pressure of the collected gas is *not* the atmospheric pressure (P_{bar}), even though the equality of the liquid levels indicates that the *total* internal pressure is equal to P_{bar}. For this total internal pressure is made up of the sum of the partial pressure of the gas in question (p_G) and the vapor pressure (p_L) exerted by the liquid over which the gas is collected. Thus the actual pressure of the gas in question is less than the barometric pressure by the margin of p_L. That is, $p_G = P_{\text{bar}} - p_L$. If the measurement is made at some temperature $T \neq 273°\text{K}$, the STP volume of the collected gas is then given as

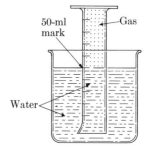

Figure 2–8

$$V_{\text{STP}} = \frac{P_{\text{bar}} - p_L}{760} \frac{273}{T} \, 50,$$

and the neglect of the correction term p_L may represent a significant error. Thus, for example, if the measurement is made over water at room temperature, p_L approximates 20 mm, and we make an error approaching 3% if we neglect this term in comparison with the prevailing barometric pressure of about 760 mm.

The Kinetic Theory

In Boyle's, Charles', Amontons', Graham's, and Dalton's laws we find empirical generalizations of great practical utility. However, it is not their practical utility that concerns us now but, rather, the theoretical significance of their mere existence. In Chapter 1 the challenge to our understanding posed by a similar set of generalizations led us to formulate an atomic-molecular theory that explains them; here the similar challenge posed by the gas laws leads us to conceive a kinetic theory of gases framed on the following postulates.

1. A gas is a space very *thinly* populated by minute particles.
2. These particles are in continuous, rapid, erratic motion conformable with Newton's laws, and their collisions with the walls of the container produce the "pressure" exerted by the gas.
3. The particles are completely *independent* in their motions, the only interaction between them being collisions supposed perfectly elastic —as are also the collisions of the particles with the container walls.
4. The *average* energy of translational motion of the gas particles is proportional to the absolute temperature of the gas.

The three words italicized in the above postulates point toward qualifying considerations that will be examined presently.

Regarding Postulate 1, observe the emphasis upon the idea that a gas is largely empty space. This idea is suggested by the observation that the densities of gases under ordinary pressures are *far* less than the densities of liquids and solids under comparable conditions. Thus, for example, the old observation that one cubic inch of water yields at its boiling point approximately one cubic foot of steam at once implies the conclusion that the density of gaseous water is only about one-seventeenhundredth of the density of liquid water. Even more to the point, if interpreted in atomistic terms, the same observation further implies [*Query:* How?] that in water vapor the center-to-center distance between adjacent molecules is 12 times the corresponding distance in liquid water. The thought that a gas is mostly empty space is still further suggested by the high compressibility of gases compared with that of liquids and solids. If in liquids and solids the particles are relatively tightly packed together, we readily understand why liquids and solids are relatively incompressible; if in gases the particles are widely separated, we readily understand how compression might crowd them closer together (and how the introduction of one gas into another might take place without change of the partial pressure of either).

Regarding Postulate 2, the assumption that the random particle motions conform to Newton's laws is readily understandable. Having demonstrated that these laws are superbly competent to explain the motions of larger particles, e.g. planets, cannonballs, etc., we follow Newton in daring to suppose that the same laws can be extrapolated into the microcosm. Observe also that the mechanism here proposed for the origin of "pressure" suggests the possibility of construing "pressure" in terms of the dynamical parameters of the particles producing it. And, in this mechanism, we find a welcome opportunity to give at least a qualitative explanation of Boyle's law. For, if more particles are crowded into a given space, by decreasing the volume, there will surely be more frequent collisions with the walls of the container and, thence, a higher pressure.

In Postulate 3, the stipulation of *elastic* collisions is required by the observation that gases do not progressively "settle" with the passage of time, as they certainly would if energy of motion were lost through inelastic collisions. The stipulation that there are no forces of interaction between the particles, save in their collisions with each other, is very strongly suggested by Dalton's law: if there *were* specific interparticle attractive or repulsive forces, we could hardly expect that, in a gaseous mixture, each gas would continue to exert its own partial pressure even in the presence of the particles of another gas or gases.

Postulate 4 is a crucial one, for it expresses the fundamental concept of "heat as a mode of motion." We may state this postulate algebraically as $\frac{1}{2}m\bar{u}^2 = KT$, where m is the mass of the particle, $\bar{u}$ is the average speed,* T is the absolute temperature, and K is a proportionality constant. Observe that an array of gas particles, occupying a fixed volume, should (in qualitative agreement with Amontons' law) exert a greater pressure as the temperature rises, because at higher temperatures collisions with the walls must be both more frequent and more vigorous. A matter of greater importance is the character of the proportionality constant K. Nothing said so far excludes the possibility that K is different for each species of gaseous particle. However, Dalton's law implies that it is a *universal* constant, for the following reason. If each gas in a mixture continues to exert its own partial pressure, regardless of the presence of others, then there can have been no *net* transfer of translational kinetic energy from one species of gas particle to another when, at constant temperature, the different species were brought together in the mixture. Yet the different species of particles are in constant collision with one another, and a net transfer of energy from

---

* Strictly speaking, $\bar{u}$ is not the simple average defined by the function $\sum \eta_i u_i / \eta$, where η is the total number of gas particles present and η_i is the number that possess each particular speed u_i. Rather, $\bar{u}$ is the so-called root-mean-square speed, defined by the function $\sqrt{\sum \eta_i u_i^2 / \eta}$, which is about 8% greater than the simple average. This difference is small enough to be inconsequential to our present concerns; the reason such a difference exists is noted on p. 158.

one species of particle to another *would* inevitably take place if, at the given temperature, the different species had different average translational energies. Thus Dalton's law, implying that no net transfer of kinetic energy *does* take place, signifies that at a given temperature *all* species of gas particles have the *same* average kinetic energy of translational motion—and that, therefore, K is the same for all gases.

This unforeseeably simple conclusion has a crucial importance that will emerge when we come to reconsider the status of Avogadro's hypothesis. Since, then, so much hinges on the alleged universality of K, we should assure ourselves that this conclusion does not rest on a misconception. From Dalton's law we infer that the partial pressure of a gas—and, hence, the average translational energy of its particles—remains unchanged in the presence of other gases. *A priori* it seems not impossible that there *is* a net transfer of energy from one species of particle to another, and that we have only an *appearance* of unchanging partial pressures when in fact (due to a net energy transfer in collisions) the partial pressure of one gas is increased while that of the other undergoes a corresponding decrease. That the increases and decreases should compensate each other so exactly, producing the additivity of nominal partial pressures expressed in Dalton's law, is assuredly a coincidence remarkable enough to excite skepticism. Yet we may still feel driven to seek some more decisive reason for rejecting the possibility that such compensation exists—and such a reason is easily found.

The apparatus sketched in Fig. 2–9 contains two chambers separated from each other only by a palladium membrane, which shows highly selective permeability to gaseous hydrogen alone. If we introduce pure hydrogen into just one of the chambers, we find that the gas pressure in it declines progressively, while the gas pressure in the other chamber under-

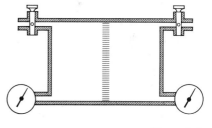

Figure 2–9

goes a corresponding increase (from its initial value of zero). An unchanging state of equilibrium is finally attained only when the pressure of hydrogen in both chambers becomes the same. At this point, without at all changing the hydrogen content of the equilibrium system, let us add to the chamber on the left some quantity of another gas (for example, argon) to which the membrane is impermeable. We find then that the pressure of hydrogen indicated by the gage on the right chamber remains *unchanged*. Now our preliminary trials convince us that if the hydrogen pressures on either side of the membrane are at all different, a net transfer of hydrogen *will* take place, with consequent change of the observed pressures. Hence, the absence of any change in the hydrogen pressure in the right-hand chamber, after the addition of argon to the left-hand chamber, becomes a very strong indication that the addition of argon has produced *no* change in the partial pressure of the hydrogen in the left chamber. That is, in such a gas mixture we are *not* dealing with some miraculously compensated changes of partial pressure. On the contrary, the addition of another gas (or gases) to the hydrogen *has* left its partial pressure unchanged. Many such experiments, in which argon may be replaced by *any* gas that does not react with hydrogen or palladium, strongly support what we have taken to be the most obvious connotation of Dalton's law.

Writing our fourth postulate in the form $\frac{1}{2}m\bar{u}^2 = KT$, we know now that the same proportionality constant K applies to all species of gaseous particles, since all such species have, at the same temperature, the same average translational kinetic energy. For many purposes it is convenient to substitute for K the expression $\frac{3}{2}k$. Nothing forbids such a substitution: k is simply a new proportionality constant $(=\frac{2}{3}K)$ and, like K itself, a constant equally applicable to all gases. Thus, as a final expression of the fourth postulate, we write

$$\tfrac{1}{2}m\bar{u}^2 = \tfrac{3}{2}kT,$$

where k is a *universal* constant commonly called the *Boltzmann* constant.

The gas laws derived. We have stated, explained, and argued for the plausibility of the postulates of the kinetic theory. But ultimately such arguments count for nothing. The proof of the theory is in the deriving— of the various empirical regularities it is designed to explain. Our first effort will be to determine the pressure on the walls of a container, produced by the bombardment of these walls by gas particles within the container. To facilitate this derivation, we begin with a brief account of the *resolution* of velocity (a vector quantity) into three mutually perpendicular components.

Consider a particle moving with velocity u, and momentarily occupying some point O within a rectangular box. Line u is drawn with length proportional to the velocity u, and with direction (in three dimensions) the same as that in which the particle is moving. Inspection of Fig. 2–10 suggests that we may consider the total velocity as made up of three component velocities (u_x, u_y, and u_z) directed along three axes radiating

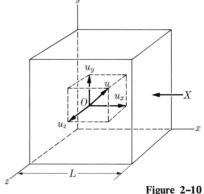

Figure 2–10

from O and parallel to the edges of the box. That is, we consider that *if* the particle had velocity u_x in the x-direction, u_y in the y-direction, and u_z in the z-direction, *then* in unit time it would reach precisely the same point as it would if it had proceeded with velocity u in the indicated direction. The *net* movement is the same in both cases. Thus the velocity u is resolved into the three component velocities and, with the aid of the Pythagorean theorem, we conclude that

$$u_x^2 + u_y^2 + u_z^2 = u^2.$$

For an assemblage of *many* particles moving *independently* with average total speed $\bar{u}$, we can write the corresponding equation

$$\bar{u}_x^2 + \bar{u}_y^2 + \bar{u}_z^2 = \bar{u}^2.$$

where $\bar{u}_x$, $\bar{u}_y$, and $\bar{u}_z$ represent the average magnitudes of the components in the x-, y-, and z-directions. If these directions are fundamentally symmetric and equivalent, as they are in the system that will concern us, those average component magnitudes must be equal. In that case we can rewrite our last equation as

$$3\bar{u}_x^2 = \bar{u}^2,$$

whence it follows that

$$\bar{u}_x^2 = \tfrac{1}{3}\bar{u}^2.$$

Consider now that, within a cubic box of linear dimension L (cm), we have a *single* gas particle with mass m (gm) and velocity u (cm/sec). In terms of u_x, the component of velocity in the x-direction, we can readily evaluate the force arising from the collisions of the particle with face X of the container shown in Fig. 2–10. All collisions having been stipulated as perfectly elastic, the particle striking wall X with velocity $+u_x$ rebounds with the numerically equal but oppositely directed velocity $-u_x$. In Newtonian mechanics we may define *force* as the rate of change of momentum, i.e. the change of momentum in unit time. (The equivalent definition of force, as mass times acceleration, is considered in the next footnote.) Momentum is also a vector quantity, and the x-component of momentum is simply mu_x. Just before its collision with wall X the particle has momentum $(m)(+u_x)$; immediately after rebounding, it has momentum $(m)(-u_x) = -mu_x$. Thus, in each collision at this wall, the particle suffers a change of momentum equal to $-2mu_x$. How many such collisions will it make in unit time? Between any two successive collisions with wall X the particle must travel a distance of $2L$ cm parallel to the x-direction, and it travels in this direction at a speed of u_x cm/sec. Obviously, then, the particle will strike wall X just $u_x/2L$ times per second. In each of these $u_x/2L$ collisions the particle undergoes a change of momentum equal to $-2mu_x$: hence in unit time the particle's total change of x-momentum at wall X is $-2mu_x^2/2L$, or $-mu_x^2/L$. Consequently, the force exerted by wall X on the particle is also $-mu_x^2/L$.* By Newton's third law of motion, the particle exerts on the wall an equal but oppositely directed force (F_x) given by

$$F_x = +mu_x^2/L.$$

Of course we never have just one particle in a box; ordinarily some very large number (η) of particles will be present. Symbolizing by $\bar{u}_x$ the *average* x-component in the assemblage of particles, we represent the average force exerted on the wall by one particle as

$$F_x = +m\bar{u}_x^2/L.$$

Other things being equal, for every 1 wall collision made by 1 particle, η wall collisions will be made by η particles†. Hence, when the box contains not 1 but η particles, we will write

$$F_x = +\eta m\bar{u}_x^2/L.$$

Pressure (P) is force per unit area, and the area of face X of the cubic box is L^2. Therefore

$$P = \frac{F_x}{L^2} = \frac{\eta m\bar{u}_x^2}{L^3}.$$

But L^3 is simply the volume (V) of the box, so that

$$PV = \eta m\bar{u}_x^2.$$

---

* If the definition of force as mass times acceleration seems more congenial, you can obtain the same result by way of this definition. In each collision at wall X the particle suffers a loss of velocity equal to $-2u_x$. In unit time the particle makes $u_x/2L$ collisions with wall X. Hence in unit time the total change of velocity suffered by the particle in its collisions with wall X is $-2u_x^2/2L$. By definition, acceleration is the change of velocity per unit time. Hence the acceleration of the particle at wall X is $-2u_x^2/2L$, and the corresponding force (equal to mass times acceleration) is $-2mu_x^2/2L = -mu_x^2/L$.

† To be sure, a collision with another particle may delay the collision of some one particle with the wall toward which it is moving. But then the *other* particle will hit that wall correspondingly sooner. Thus in the indicated head-on collision of A with B for example,

A is turned back from a collision with wall X that it would otherwise have made; but, correspondingly, B is turned back to make a collision with X that it would otherwise *not* have made. The total change of momentum at wall X remains exactly the same.

Having found earlier that $\bar{u}_x^2 = \frac{1}{3}\bar{u}^2$, we can then substitute to find

$$PV = \frac{1}{3}\eta m\bar{u}^2. \tag{a}$$

This is a fundamental formula well worth remembering. Though the "derivation" we have given is seriously lacking in rigor, a more elaborate and formally impeccable derivation yields the same result.

We can press one last step further with the aid of our fourth postulate. That postulate we expressed in the equation $\frac{1}{2}m\bar{u}^2 = \frac{3}{2}kT$, where k is a universal proportionality constant. Substituting on the strength of this relation, we write

$$PV = (\tfrac{2}{3}\eta)(\tfrac{1}{2}m\bar{u}^2) = (\tfrac{2}{3}\eta)(\tfrac{3}{2}kT) = \eta kT$$

or

$$PV/T = \eta k. \tag{b}$$

In a given parcel of gas the number of particles (η) is a constant, and k has been defined as a constant. Therefore, the right side of the last equation is a constant. For a given gas sample, then, PV/T must also be constant. But this is just what is found empirically; it represents the *total* content of Boyle's, Charles', and Amontons' laws. This is a major triumph for the kinetic theory. From it we have derived, and to this extent *explained*, the three most familiar gas laws.

Aiming at Graham's law, we may begin with equation (a), which we rewrite as

$$P = \frac{1}{3}\frac{\eta m}{V}\bar{u}^2.$$

What does the function $\eta m/V$ represent? The numerator expresses the total mass of the gas with which we are concerned, i.e. the number of particles of gas present times the mass of one particle; the denominator expresses the total volume over which the mass is distributed. Hence, the quotient $\eta m/V$ represents the density (δ) of the gas in question. Suppose now that we wish to compare two gases (A and B) held under the same working pressure (P). For them we can write

$$\tfrac{1}{3}\delta_A\bar{u}_A^2 = P = \tfrac{1}{3}\delta_B\bar{u}_B^2$$

or

$$\bar{u}_A/\bar{u}_B = \sqrt{\delta_B/\delta_A}\,.$$

Denoting by r_A and r_B the volume-rates of effusion of gases A and B, we now venture to write

$$r_A/r_B = \bar{u}_A/\bar{u}_B.$$

That the rates of effusion should stand to each other in the same ratio as the average speeds of the effusing particles is certainly not implausible, but we are here simply *asserting* a relation for which a proper *demonstration* would be a very considerable (though perfectly feasible) undertaking. Provided that the assertion is accepted, the last two equations can be combined to yield Graham's law:

$$r_A/r_B = \sqrt{\delta_B/\delta_A} \, .$$

Turning now to Dalton's law, consider a specimen of gas A in sole occupancy of volume V at temperature T. For it we write

$$p_A = \frac{1}{3V} \, \eta_A m_A \bar{u}_A^2 = \frac{1}{V} \, \eta_A kT.$$

For a specimen of gas B under the same conditions, we have

$$p_B = \frac{1}{3V} \, \eta_B m_B \bar{u}_B^2 = \frac{1}{V} \, \eta_B kT.$$

Now consider that both specimens are put together in the *same* volume V, at a temperature T maintained constant. Given the universality of the constant k, each species of gas particle retains its kinetic energy unchanged. If "pressure" is conceived as resultant from particle impacts, the total pressure (P_{AB}) is surely expressible as the following sum:

$$P_{AB} = \frac{1}{3V} \, \eta_A m_A \bar{u}_A^2 + \frac{1}{3V} \, \eta_B m_B \bar{u}_B^2.$$

But then substitution from the two preceding equations promptly yields

$$P_{AB} = p_A + p_B$$

and, for an n-component mixture,

$$P_{\text{mixt}} = \Sigma p_i.$$

These successes encourage confidence in our kinetic theory. Given that confidence, we may rely on the kinetic theory to resolve the difficult question with which we began this chapter: *Is Avogadro's hypothesis sound?* That question can easily be answered at this point. Consider two gases, A and B, for which equation (b) gives us

$$\frac{P_A V_A}{T_A} = \eta_A k$$

and

$$\frac{P_B V_B}{T_B} = \eta_B k.$$

Let us assume that we have equal volumes of the two gases, measured at equal temperatures and pressures. We may then write

$$P_A = P_B, \qquad V_A = V_B, \qquad T_A = T_B.$$

And then

$$\frac{P_A V_A}{T_A} = \frac{P_B V_B}{T_B},$$

so that

$$\eta_A k = \eta_B k.$$

Therefore, since the constant k is the same for all gases, we readily conclude that

$$\eta_A = \eta_B.$$

We have thus *derived* from the principles of a kinetic theory, whose other successes give us strong reasons for trusting it, what had previously been only Avogadro's *hypothesis*, but which will hereafter be called Avogadro's *rule*. That is, we have demonstrated that equal volumes of two gases, measured at the same temperature and pressure, contain equal numbers of the respective gas particles.

Real Gases and Ideal Gases

With Avogadro's rule (no longer a hypothesis) well established on the strength of the kinetic theory, all difficulties encountered earlier in our attempt to interpret Gay-Lussac's-law data melt away. Yet we may be well advised to defer this deployment of Avogadro's rule. For we cannot adequately appraise the standing of the rule until we have conducted a more searching appraisal of the strength of the kinetic theory from which it has been derived. To that examination we now proceed.

We set out from certain gas laws, empirical generalizations we took to be exact. We devised a kinetic theory of gases, and we carried through derivations that yielded the gas laws as necessary deductions from our theory. It may then seem embarrassing that although our theory appears to *require* the gas laws to be exact, more searching experimental investigation reveals that they are only approximate. However, there is here no occasion for dismay, but only a quite typical illustration of a general mode of scientific progress. Always we begin with rather simple laws we think exact. Ordinarily we find that some relatively simple theory is quite sufficient to rationalize these empirical regularities. If later we find that the laws are only approximate, they will already have served a useful purpose. For they have led us to a theory we might well have failed to achieve had we been confronted at the outset with the *full* complexity of natural phenomena. When such complexities arise only later, we face them armed with *a theory already in existence*. We recognize that the simple theory is,

TABLE 2–1

Substance	Normal boiling point, °K	Critical temperature, °K
Hydrogen	20.4	33.3
Nitrogen	77.3	126.1
Oxygen	90.1	154.3
Carbon dioxide	194.6(s)	304.2
Ammonia	239.7	405.6
Water	373.15	647.3

to some degree, an *over*simplification. But, provided that it *is* basically sound, we have then only to consider the generally minor modifications needed to make it render a full account of natural phenomena somewhat more complex than we at first imagined. The simple kinetic theory we have outlined *is* basically sound, and we do not need to look very far to see those refinements that, when made, will permit us to render just account of the *inexactitude* of the gas laws formerly regarded (and derived) as exact.

For each known gas, we find that there is some maximum temperature above which it cannot be condensed to a liquid, however high the pressure under which it is held. This maximum temperature is called the *critical temperature*, or critical point, for the gas in question. To the critical temperature there correspond a critical pressure (representing the minimum pressure required to produce condensation at the critical point) and a critical volume (representing the volume of one mole of the condensed phase so produced). Each gas has its own characteristic set of these three *critical constants*—just as it has its own normal boiling point, i.e. that temperature at which the gas condenses under a pressure of 1 atm. Some representative data are displayed in Table 2–1, and we shall refer to these data presently. For the moment, however, the crucially important thing is a purely qualitative observation.

We find that all real gases condense at a temperature above 0°K, and often quite far above 0°K, to liquids (or solids) having volumes that, however small, are perfectly significant. This one statement points toward the two major elements of oversimplification in our basic theory.

First: We regarded a gas as a space *thinly* populated with particles, and made no allowance for the possibility that these particles themselves *fill* a finite volume. This is clearly more than a mere possibility: it is a certainty. After all, one cubic foot of steam at atmospheric pressure *does* yield approximately one cubic inch of water—which we may regard as a *crude* indication of the "excluded volume" actually occupied by an assembly of water molecules closely packed together in the liquid state. Here, as in every other case, we surely oversimplify when we work, as we have, with a theory that treats molecules as point-masses rather than as bodies of finite bulk. Now, in the total volume taken up by a gas at 1 atm pressure, the "excluded volume" will represent a very small fraction (ca. 1/1700 in the case of steam at atmospheric pressure). However, if we are dealing with a gas above its critical point, we can compress it as highly as we please—and the excluded volume must ultimately come to represent a substantial fraction of the total volume assumed by the gas. As the pressure is increased, less and less of the gas space is actually free space into which the molecules can be crowded by further compression, and so the gas must prove *less* compressible than would be predicted from Boyle's law. The behavior of a gas highly compressed at a constant temperature far above its critical point is indeed that shown in Fig. 2–11. Where the ideal (point-mass) gas would give a straight horizontal line on a plot of PV vs. P, the real gas (e.g. hydrogen at room temperature) gives a line sloping upward.

The real gas *is* less compressible than an ideal gas: a doubling of the gas pressure does *not* suffice to halve the gas volume. The effect is most pronounced at high pressures, as is to be expected. But, if we use methods of sufficient delicacy, we find that even at low pressures, a gas well above its critical point is *always* a gas less compressible than Boyle's law predicts: i.e. the PV-product increases slightly with increase in P.

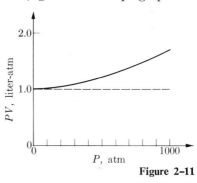

Figure 2–11

Second: We regarded a gas as composed of wholly *independent* particles, and made no allowance for the possibility that these particles act on one another quite apart from their mutual collisions. Actually the possibility that there are weak attractive forces acting between the particles is also far more than a possibility: it is a certainty. For consider that at any temperature above $0°K$ the gas particles have finite kinetic energies that tend to keep them dispersed throughout the space available to them. But since every gas condenses to a liquid (or solid) at temperatures above $0°K$, it is clear that there *must* be active among the gas particles attractive forces capable of overcoming the dispersive effect of molecular motions, to the point of aggregating the particles in a compact liquid (or solid). These attractive forces are weak: for each gas their maximum strength is barely sufficient to override the average kinetic energy possessed by the particles at the critical temperature of that gas. However, to the extent that such forces are at all effective, it is clear that they will render the gas *more* compressible than an ideal gas would be. When a real gas is subjected to moderate compression, at a temperature not far above its critical point, a doubling of the pressure cuts the volume to *less* than one-half its initial value. Beyond the volume decrease due purely to the increase in applied pressure, a *further* volume decrease arises from the action of forces working to draw the particles more closely together.

We have then *two* effects active in nonideal gases; one acting to make the *PV*-product too large, the other acting to make the *PV*-product too small. How do these effects combine to produce the observed behavior of real gases? Since the effects are both individually small *and* opposed to each other, real gases under moderate pressures display a very good approximation to the simple behavior described by Boyle's law. But what behavior will we observe when we make accurate measurements at moderate pressures, or even moderately accurate measurements at high pressures? Everything depends on the margin of difference between our working temperature and the critical temperature for the gas concerned.

Consider a real gas at a temperature far above its critical temperature. The kinetic energy of the gas particles then far outweighs the intermolecular attractive forces, and these forces cannot make themselves much felt. The predominant effect is then that due to the finite bulk of the molecules—and the observed behavior of the gas assumes the form shown in the preceding figure. Next consider a real gas at a temperature not very far above its critical point. In that case the intermolecular attractions may well be comparable to the average kinetic energy of the particles, and this effect (*increasing* the compressibility of the gas) is dominant at low pressures. But, when the gas has been sufficiently compressed, the excluded volume must ultimately come to represent a substantial fraction of the total gas volume. Thus at sufficiently high pressure this second effect (*decreasing* the compressibility of the gas) must become dominant. We have then the kind of behavior crudely sketched in curve *L* of Fig. 2–12. Clearly, the same gas may give quite different curves, depending on the temperature at which it is studied. At temperatures comparable to its critical temperature it may follow curve *L*; at intermediate temperatures it may follow a curve like *I*; and at high temperatures, a curve like *H*. Thus, as the temperature is progressively increased, we find an entire family of intermediate curve forms including one (corresponding to the so-called "Boyle temperature" of the gas) which is, for some considerable range of pressures, a good approximation to the horizontal straight line representing simple Boyle's-law behavior. If, on the other hand, we con-

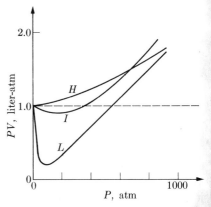

Figure 2

sider *different* gases at the *same* temperature, we find for each a curve determined by the extent to which the chosen temperature exceeds the critical temperature of that gas. Thus at room temperature, something like curve L might represent the behavior of carbon dioxide (critical temperature $T_c = 304°K$), curve I might represent oxygen ($T_c = 153.4°K$), and curve H might represent hydrogen ($T_c = 33.3°K$).

Treating gas particles as *independent point-masses*, we found that our simple kinetic theory entails Boyle's law, etc., as rigorously exact expressions. In fact, we may well regard them *as* rigorous—for the hypothetical ideal gas constituted of particles perfectly conformable with the specifications expressed in our model. But actual gases, *real* gases, are made up of particles whose behavior is only a more or less close approximation to the behavior of ideal-gas particles. And, indeed, the *form* of the deviations of real gases from Boyle's law is, as indicated above, qualitatively in line with what we would predict on the basis of a kinetic theory that adopts a more sophisticated model for real (as distinct from ideal) gases. In this model the particles of real gases are regarded as particles of finite bulk, acting upon each other with small but finite attractive forces. To make rigorous deductions from this more elaborate model is exceedingly difficult. But surely enough has been said to show that, in principle, this more sophisticated theory should be competent to explain both the approximation to, and the deviations from, the simple behavior expressed in Boyle's law. To the extent that the particles of a real gas approximate those of an ideal gas, the real gas will conform to Boyle's law, which is rigorously derivable for an ideal gas. To the extent that the particles of a real gas differ from those of an ideal gas, the real gas will deviate from Boyle's law, and the qualitative form of the deviation is theoretically predictable.

We have taken Boyle's law as exemplar of *all* the gas laws. All these laws—rigorous as applied to ideal gases—are only approximate as applied to real gases, and for the same reasons discussed in the case of Boyle's law. And now a disturbing question presents itself. We propose to build much on the application of Avogadro's rule to real gases, but we have derived Avogadro's rule only for the hypothetical ideal gas. We should then expect just what we will find: like all the simple gas laws derived on the ideal-gas model, Avogadro's rule is also only approximate as applied to real gases. How serious is this shortcoming? At or around room temperature and atmospheric pressure, the simple gas laws rarely fail by a margin exceeding 2 or 3%. It is not then unreasonable to suppose that Avogadro's rule— which involves in its derivation exactly the same assumptions used in deriving the gas laws—may also fall short of accuracy to the extent of 2 or 3%. This may well seem to spell the ruin of our entire endeavor to obtain *accurate* atomic weights by way of a calculation involving Avogadro's rule. However, this is not at all the case—for reasons now to be considered.

Gay-Lussac's Law and Avogadro's Rule

We begin by supposing that real gases behave as though they were ideal gases, to which Avogadro's rule is exactly applicable. In this case we can easily develop the line of argument needed to establish the atomic weights of the gaseous elements, and the formulas of their gaseous compounds. And then, recalling that real gases are *not* ideal and that Avogadro's rule applies only as an approximation to real gases, we review the argument to see what (very minor) modifications are required when it must be carried on under these more difficult conditions.

To the extent that Avogadro's rule is exact, we may be sure that under CTP conditions, *anything that can be said about relative numbers of volumes of gases can be said also about relative numbers of gaseous particles, and conversely.* For each unit volume must, we know, contain the same number (η) of the gaseous particles in question. Thus, given as an empirical finding that

2 volumes hydrogen $+$ 1 volume oxygen $\rightarrow$ 2 volumes water vapor,

we can at once write

2η hydrogen particles $+$ η oxygen particles $\rightarrow$ 2η particles water vapor

or

2 hydrogen particles $+$ 1 oxygen particle $\rightarrow$ 2 particles water vapor.

The atom being indivisible, each water-vapor particle must contain *at least one* oxygen atom. And Avogadro's rule now assures us, as Avogadro's hypothesis could not, that two water-vapor particles *are* formed for each oxygen particle that reacts—which entails the further conclusion that each oxygen particle contains *at least two* oxygen atoms. Other even numbers are possible, but no odd number need be considered. For observe that if the oxygen particle contained an odd number of atoms, these could not be evenly divided among the two water-vapor particles produced. If, for example, the oxygen particle contained three oxygen atoms, we would at best obtain one water-vapor particle containing two oxygen atoms and another containing only one oxygen atom. In this case we would have two distinct species of water-vapor particles that, with so gross a difference in their constitution, would have properties different enough to make them readily distinguishable. But experimentally we find no such heterogeneity of character in water vapor, all particles of which appear to behave alike. Hence each must contain the *same* number of oxygen atoms, and the number of oxygen atoms per oxygen particle must be *even*. But the range of possibilities then still remains deplorably broad. At this point we know nothing about the number of oxygen atoms present per water molecule: it might be one, but it might also be two, three, etc. All we can write is

$$2 \text{ hydrogen particles} + O_b \rightarrow 2H_?O_{b/2},$$

where b is an unknown even number.*

What about the hydrogen? Must we consider the possibility that the hydrogen particle also contains more than one atom? The above reaction sheds no light on this point, but we are well aware of another reaction that does:

1 volume hydrogen + 1 volume chlorine $\rightarrow$ 2 volumes hydrogen chloride

or

1 hydrogen particle + 1 chlorine particle
$$\rightarrow 2 \text{ hydrogen-chloride particles.}$$

From this result it follows, by exactly the same line of argument given above for oxygen, that the formula of the hydrogen particle must be H_a, where a is some *even* number. We can then take one further step in interpreting the combining-volume data for the formation of water vapor, by writing

$$2H_a + O_b \rightarrow 2H_aO_{b/2}.$$

Observe that whatever the value of a, the number of hydrogen atoms per water-vapor particle and per gaseous-hydrogen particle must in any case remain the *same*.

This is progress of a sort, but to progress any further we must call on some additional data to establish values for a and b. Consider the possibility that the hydrogen particle contains four hydrogen atoms. That hypothesis yields a specific prediction. **If** we study a sufficient variety of reactions in which gaseous hydrogen reacts with some nonhydrogenous species (atomic or molecular, and not itself necessarily gaseous) to give a gaseous product containing hydrogen, **then** we should, sooner or later, encounter a case in which the reaction of *one* volume of gaseous hydrogen yields *four* volumes of a gaseous hydrogenous product. In effect, this prediction builds on the perfectly plausible *assumption* that we must sooner or later encounter at least one hydrogenous product containing just one

---

* We have, of course, assumed that the number b is the *same* for all oxygen particles. Otherwise we would have two or more different kinds of oxygen particles in pure oxygen gas, which, however, gives no evidence whatever of any such heterogeneity of composition.

hydrogen atom per molecule of product. In this case we would have the particle relation:

$$1H_4 \xrightarrow{[Z]} 4H_1Z_x.$$

But, from Avogadro's rule, the ratio of numbers of particles must be also the ratio of gas volumes under CTP conditions. Hence

$$1 \text{ volume } H_4 \xrightarrow{[Z]} 4 \text{ volumes } HZ_x.$$

Now in fact—though we examine a great variety of reactions in which hydrogen reacts with some nonhydrogenous material to give a gaseous hydrogenous product—we *never* find a reaction with the volume relation indicated above. *No* such reaction has ever been known to give more than *two* volumes of product per volume of hydrogen used. Granting the plausibility of the indicated assumption, we have then a very strong case for concluding that the formula of the gaseous hydrogen particle is just H_2. A similar argument, founded on data obtained in a similar study of the reactions of oxygen, leads to the similar conclusion that the formula of the gaseous oxygen particle is O_2.

Having thus assigned the number 2 to both a and b, we can now rewrite our last equation for the reaction in which water vapor is formed from its elements:

$$2H_2 + O_2 \rightarrow 2H_2O.$$

And lo! We now have a self-sufficient method for establishing the formula of water—which the methods of Chapter 1 left completely in doubt. Note that the formula H_2O is a molecular formula, not just an empirical formula; but even an empirical formula would be quite sufficient. Once given a formula, the methods of Chapter 1 permit an immediate evaluation of the ratio of the atomic weights of hydrogen and oxygen. For we already know the *combining weights* in which hydrogen and oxygen unite to form water: 1 gm of hydrogen combines with 8 gm of oxygen. And then, as shown on p. 25, it at once follows that the atomic weight of hydrogen stands to that of oxygen as $1:16$ (more accurately, $1.008:16$).

The whole of the foregoing calculation is an oversimplification. It sets out from an alleged observation that exactly 2 volumes of water vapor are formed per volume of oxygen reacted, and assumes Avogadro's rule exactly applicable to real gases. The *actual* observation would be that, say, 1.95 volumes of water vapor are formed per volume of oxygen reacted, and the calculation must be conducted *without* assuming the exactitude of Avogadro's rule. *How then shall we proceed?* If, using the actual data, we were to assume the exactitude of Avogadro's rule, the observed volume ratio would imply that the molecule of gaseous oxygen contains 1.95 times as many oxygen atoms as does the water molecule. Since atoms are indivisible, this ratio must be expressed in integral numbers. But the smallest integers compatible with the indicated ratio are 39 atoms of oxygen per oxygen molecule and 20 atoms of oxygen per water molecule. Such numbers are palpably absurd, and on two distinct counts: (i) combining-weight data expressed in the laws of multiple and equivalent proportions offer strong assurance that the molecule of such a compound as water contains only *small* numbers of atoms; and (ii) combining-volume data for a great variety of reactions involving gaseous oxygen strongly suggest (*vide supra*) that the molecule of gaseous oxygen contains no more than *two* oxygen atoms. Thus we can have no hesitation in rejecting such numbers as 20 and 39. What then?

We obtained these absurd numbers only because we insisted on interpreting the volume ratio actually observed in terms of Avogadro's rule assumed *exact*. That assumption we know to be groundless. Abandoning an untenable assumption, let us proceed on the basis that Avogadro's rule is only *approximate*. Experimentally we find that 1.95 volumes of water vapor are formed for each 1.00 volume of oxygen that reacts. Given the boundary conditions (i) and (ii) above, only *one* interpretation of these data will be possible. Noting that Avogadro's rule is only approximate as applied to real gases, we must assume that the number of water molecules in 1.95 volumes of water vapor is just 2.00 times the number of oxygen molecules in 1.00 volume of gaseous oxygen. This is the only possible interpretation consistent both with the requirement that the number of oxygen atoms per water molecule be a small whole number, and with the requirement that the number 2 shall represent the number of oxygen atoms per molecule of gaseous oxygen. Thus *we obtain exactly the same conclusion* whether we take Avogadro's rule as exact in its application to idealized data (that is, 2.00 volumes of water vapor per 1.00 volume of oxygen used) which we suppose we would have collected if water vapor and oxygen were ideal gases or, on the other hand, we apply Avogadro's hypothesis only as an approximation to actual data (1.95 volumes of water vapor per 1.00 volume of oxygen used).

How does it happen that in the second case we can still draw a mathematically precise conclusion even while denying the rigor of a rule used in drawing that conclusion? A moment's consideration shows that this is possible only because we can feel quite certain that the answer, whatever it is, must conform to the two boundary conditions noted above. For it is precisely these restrictions that permit us to pass, from the observed 1.95 to 1.00 ratio of volumes, to the inferred 1.00 to 2.00 inverse ratio of atoms per gaseous particle. And the same or equivalent boundary conditions are active at *every* subsequent stage of our derivation of the formula of water. Such boundary conditions serve to complement Avogadro's rule, and eliminate all uncertainty arising from the inexactitude of that rule as applied to real gases. Moreover, once we have established the *formula* of the water molecule in this way, we make *no further use* of Avogadro's rule in calculating the relative atomic weights. Given this formula, we can easily calculate those atomic weights from *combining-weight* data alone. Hence, even though Avogadro's rule is only approximate as applied to real gases, it suffices to open up a route to relative atomic weights as accurate as the combining-weight data from which they are ultimately calculated.

At last we have broken into the refractory triangular array. Let joy be unconfined? Well, not *quite* unconfined. Observe that the method we have developed can be applied only to *gaseous elements that form many gaseous compounds.* Our method works well for hydrogen, nitrogen, oxygen, and chlorine, and it can easily be extended to such other readily gasifiable elements as bromine and iodine. In such cases we can establish the molecular formulas of the gaseous elements, the molecular formulas of their gaseous compounds (and the empirical formulas of their nongaseous compounds), and thence, by use of combining-weight data, the accurate relative atomic weights of the elements concerned. But, alas, these triumphs *cannot* be extended to the vast majority of elements, which are neither gaseous nor readily gasifiable. Clearly our breakthrough is still seriously incomplete. To complete it we must call on other methods to be discussed in Chapter 3. Before going on, however, let us consolidate the position already attained.

The molar volume. We have assumed that like the gas laws, Avogadro's rule, when applied to real gases at room temperature and pressure, is accurate to within a few percent. It will be well to cross check this assumption by way of the results to which it leads. Having in hand accurate atomic weights for hydrogen, oxygen, nitrogen, etc., and knowing the molecular formulas of such gaseous elements and compounds as H_2, O_2, N_2, Cl_2, NO, NH_3, HCl, etc., we can now regard the *molecular weights* of such species as well established.* From these molecular weights, we know how many grams of each substance constitute one mole of that substance. Now, we saw in Chapter 1 that one mole of any substance always contains the same number of particles. But then, to the extent that Avogadro's rule is sound, one mole of *any* gaseous substance should always occupy the *same* STP volume. We can, then, estimate the soundness of Avogadro's rule by examining the agreement of the molar volumes for different substances of known molecular weight.

---

* These atomic and molecular weights can only be established relative to the standard set by taking the atomic weight of oxygen as 16.0, since our method cannot be extended to an involatile element like carbon. However, $O \equiv 16.0$ is a perfectly satisfactory reference standard and, indeed, served as such for well over a century—until, only a few years ago, the atomic-weight scale based on $C \equiv 12.0$ was first adopted. Actually, as we will see, the two scales are self-consistent to a high degree of approximation.

TABLE 2–2

Substance	H_2	N_2	O_2	Cl_2	NH_3	NO	HCl
STP molar volume in liters	22.43	22.40	22.39	22.06	22.09	22.39	22.25

How can we determine molar volumes? We need only measure the density of each gas at a temperature and pressure not too far removed from 273°K and 1 atm pressure.* Let us take oxygen (O_2) as our example, and let us suppose that we find (by an experimental method noted in the very next section) that the density of oxygen is 1.3139 gm/liter at 20°C and 75.00 cm Hg pressure. Seeking the molar volume under STP conditions, we calculate from the observed result a figure for the density of oxygen at 0°C (273.15°K) and 76.00 cm Hg. What is the STP volume of the 1.000 liter of oxygen measured at 293.15°K and 75.00 cm Hg?

$$V_{STP} = \frac{273.15}{293.15} \cdot \frac{75.00}{76.00} \cdot 1.000 = 0.9194 \text{ liter.}$$

The weight of this STP volume of oxygen is 1.3139 gm. Hence, the STP density of oxygen is $1.3139/0.9194 = 1.429$ gm/liter. To find the STP *molar* volume of oxygen we have then only to determine the volume occupied by 32.00 gm of oxygen, which is $32.00/1.429 = 22.39$ liters. Similar calculations, based on measured gas densities of the other substances whose molecular weights we have established, yield the results shown in Table 2–2. These results permit us to see at a glance that Avogadro's rule *is* a good approximation. The number 22.4, roughly representing the gram-molar volume, is a good one to keep in mind: with its aid we can always calculate, at least approximately, the number of moles represented by some given volume of gas measured at any given temperature and pressure.† How-

---

* Ideally, we would measure the density under STP conditions, so that we need make no calculations by way of gas laws that are only approximate as applied to real gases. However, we find that essentially the same result is obtained if our measurements are made at other temperatures and pressures, *provided that* they are close enough to the STP values to require no long extrapolation by way of the gas laws.

† It is of interest (and some practical convenience) to observe that 22.4 represents not only the volume in *liters* of one *gram*-mole but also the volume in *cubic feet* of one *ounce*-mole. That is, for example, 32 ounces of gaseous oxygen occupy 22.4 cubic feet STP. This curious situation arises because, just as one gram represents approximately one-thousandth part of one liter of water, the ounce was apparently defined to represent one-thousandth of one cubic foot of water (that is $62.4 \text{ lb/ft}^3 \times 16 \text{ oz/lb} \doteq 1000 \text{ oz/ft}^3$). The two sets of units agree with each other to better than the degree of approximation involved in applying the figure 22.4 to real gases.

ever, an even simpler method for making this calculation will be developed presently.

Can we hope to use Avogadro's rule to obtain accurate relative atomic weights directly from gas-density data, without ever drawing on combining-weight data? This may well seem impossible: here there are no small-whole-number boundary conditions since, unlike formulas, atomic weights may well prove (generally *do* prove) to involve numbers neither integral nor small. Unable to use such boundary conditions to make good the shortcomings of Avogadro's rule, must we then relinquish all hope of deriving accurate atomic weights from gas-density data? The obvious answer is "Yes," but the right answer is "No!" How can this be? If, working with real gases, we could discover what data they *would* yield if they *were* ideal gases, then Avogadro's rule could be rigorously applied to draw accurate relative atomic weights from relative gas-density data. Let us examine how this apparently impossible undertaking can actually be carried through.

Real Gases as Ideal in the Limit of Zero Pressure

Our derivation from the simple kinetic theory yielded the expression

$$PV/T = \eta k.$$

A mole of anything always contains the same number of particles of the species in question, which number (*Avogadro's number*) we symbolize as N. Suppose that we have present some n moles of ideal gas. For the total number of particles present we can write $\eta = nN$, whence it follows that

$$PV/T = nNk.$$

Now both N and k are universal constants, applicable to all species of (ideal) gases. For this product of universal constants, we can substitute a single constant, R, defined by the equation $R = Nk$. Our last equation then becomes

$$PV = nRT,$$

where R is also a universal constant, the magnitude of which will be established presently. For one mole of ideal gas we have simply

$$PV = RT.$$

Consider now a corresponding expression for one mole of a *real* gas. This is the equation, first proposed by van der Waals, which has the form

$$(P + a/V^2)(V - b) = RT.$$

Here a and b are constants, varying with the identity of the gas concerned, that express respectively the intermolecular-force effect and the excluded-volume effect. It is easy enough to see that this is a reasonable form of equation for a real gas. As for the excluded-volume effect, recall that it makes the gas *less* compressible than an ideal gas would be. Other things being equal, the actually measured gas volume for a real gas will then be greater than it would be were the gas ideal. When, in the expression $(V - b)$, we subtract from the measured volume the volume-correction term b, the result may plausibly be taken to represent the volume the gas would have had if it were ideal. As for the intermolecular-force effect, observe that this makes the measured pressure of a real gas *less* than that of an ideal gas; i.e., intermolecular forces, drawing back on a gas particle about to collide with a wall, must tend to reduce the impact in any such collision. A correction term for the intermolecular forces should then be *added* to the pressure actually measured. Van der Waals found that an a/V^2 term is needed to account for the progressive reduction in the effectiveness of these forces that occurs when, on increase of volume, the interacting particles become more widely separated. When, in the expression $(P + a/V^2)$, we add to the measured pressure the pressure-correction term a/V^2, the sum may be taken to represent the pressure the gas would exert if it were ideal. But if $(P + a/V^2)$ is such an ideal pressure and $(V - b)$ such an ideal volume, we should be able to equate their product to the term RT obtained earlier as equal to the PV-product of an ideal gas. Hence van der Waals' equation

$$(P + a/V^2)(V - b) = RT.$$

The values of a and b can be determined from experimental measurements of the critical constants of a real gas, and the above equation does in fact offer a better representation of the behavior of that real gas than does the uncorrected ideal-gas law. But these are not now matters of primary concern to us.

The crucial thing about van der Waals' equation (and about other such equations devised accurately to represent the PVT-behavior of real gases) is the indication that, as the pressure of a real gas approaches zero, the behavior of the real gas approaches that of an ideal gas. That is, whatever the values of a and b in the above equation, if we go to sufficiently small pressures (which is also to say sufficiently large volumes), the correction terms that represent the nonideality of the real gas must ultimately become negligible. Ultimately the b-term (which is a constant for a given gas) must become vanishingly small in comparison with a V-term that increases without limit as the pressure declines. And ultimately the a/V^2 term, which decreases as the inverse *second* power of V, must similarly become negligible in comparison with the P-term which (by Boyle's law) falls off roughly as the inverse *first* power of V. Thus **if,** having collected data on real gases at finite pressures, we can extrapolate those data to zero pressure, **then** the value corresponding to zero pressure will be an ideal-gas value, i.e. the value that *would* be obtained if the real gas described by van der Waals' equation *were* actually an ideal gas described by the equation $PV = RT$. That there is genuine substance to this highly hypothetical statement can easily be demonstrated.

We observed that the molar volumes of real gases, calculated from gas densities measured at or around atmospheric pressure, differ somewhat among themselves. Consider now that we measure the densities of the same group of gases at a variety of pressures. We can, for example, use Regnault's method. We first weigh an evacuated glass (or metal) globe (Fig. 2–13). Next we fill it with whatever gas we choose. Finally we re-weigh the globe to determine the weight of the (known) volume of gas at the (measured) temperature and pressure. We then bring to bear the gas laws to determine the STP volume of the gas weighed, and thence the STP volume that would be occupied by one mole of that gas. These measurements can obviously be repeated at as many gas pressures as we please, and in principle this is a perfectly straightforward procedure. In practice it represents an exceedingly difficult operation—if only because of the great difficulty of securing accurate values for the small weights of gas present when the pressure in the globe is reduced much below one atmosphere. However, these experiments have actually been performed. They yield the results shown in Fig. 2–14, which displays a remarkably satisfactory situation. At finite pressures the calculated STP molar volumes of real gases differ among themselves, and differ even for a given gas when its STP molar volume is determined from measurements made at various pressures.* But when we plot these data and extrapolate to zero pressure, we find that the *limiting* value of the molar volume is the same for all gases—

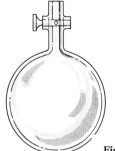

Figure 2–13

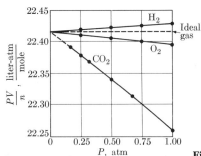

Figure 2–14

---

* With an *ideal* gas all measurements would of course yield the *same* STP molar volume.

just what we would expect to find if, as we have argued, the behavior of real gases approaches the behavior of the hypothetical ideal gas as the gas pressure approaches zero.

The gas-law constant, R. Having established that the molar volume of an ideal gas is 22.414 liters STP, we can now set a value on the universal constant R in the equation $PV = nRT$. For one mole of gas $n = 1$; for STP conditions $P = 76.00$ cm and $T = 273.15°K$. Thus we have

$$(76.00)(22.414) = (1)(R)(273.15)$$

$$R = 6.23 \text{ liter-cm Hg/mole-°K}.$$

The numerical value of R is obviously dependent on the units of pressure and volume used, and the number 6.23 is applicable *only* when pressure and volume are expressed in cm Hg and liters, respectively. Having in hand an appropriate value for R, one finds that the equation $PV = nRT$ offers a very straightforward way of calculating the number of moles of (ideal) gas corresponding to any particular volume of such gas measured under any particular conditions of temperature and pressure (see Illustrative Example on p. 70). However, such elements of practical utility are dwarfed by the profound theoretical significance attaching to the constant R.

One element of that significance, which will later prove important to us, can be developed here. Observe that the dimensions of R $(=PV/nT)$ are energy units/mole-°K. For consider that in the PV-term from which R is calculated, the dimensions of pressure are force/area $=$ force/(length)^2 and the dimensions of volume are (length)^3. Therefore PV will have the dimensions

$$\frac{\text{force}}{(\text{length})^2} \, (\text{length})^3 = \text{force} \times \text{length}$$

or force times distance, which represent the dimensions of work or energy. Thus 6.23 liter-cm Hg/mole-°K actually stands for a quantity of energy, and it is easy to show (see problem 9 on p. 74) that in more familiar energy-units, $R = 8.31$ joules/mole-°K $= 1.99$ cal/mole-°K. In terms of R, one can find a very simple expression for the translational kinetic energy of one mole of any ideal gas. For one mole of gas, equation (a) on p. 49 can be rewritten as

$$PV = \tfrac{1}{3}Nm\bar{u}^2,$$

where N represents Avogadro's number, the number of particles in one gram-mole. The corresponding expression of the ideal gas law for one mole of gas is

$$PV = (1)RT.$$

Combining the two expressions, we find that

$$\tfrac{1}{3}Nm\bar{u}^2 \;=\; RT, \qquad \tfrac{2}{3}N(\tfrac{1}{2}m\bar{u}^2) \;=\; RT.$$

Now $\tfrac{1}{2}m\bar{u}^2$ represents the average translational kinetic energy of one gas particle, and $N(\tfrac{1}{2}m\bar{u}^2)$ is then the translational kinetic energy of one mole of gas particles. Consequently

translational kinetic energy of one mole of ideal gas $= \tfrac{3}{2}RT$.

The temperature scale revisited. An extrapolation to zero pressure makes it possible, we alleged, to obtain ideal results from measurements made on real gases. Applying this style of extrapolation to (different) molar volumes actually measured for real gases at finite pressures, we have found the expected convergence on a single (ideal) value. We wish to deploy this extrapolation in a determination of accurate atomic weights but, before attacking that problem, we may do well to confirm, in at least one other case, that such extrapolation does yield the expected convergence in the limit of zero pressure. We earlier remarked (p. 39) the possibility of basing an absolute scale of temperature on the application of Amontons' law to readings obtained with a gas thermometer. However, Amontons' law applies rigorously only to ideal gases, and we have only real gases with which to charge our thermometers. Little wonder, then, that we find slightly different values for, say, the normal boiling point of water when—having established our scale by assigning 273.15°K as the melting point of ice*—we use gas thermometers charged with different real gases. Our values scatter badly around 373°K when we solve for T_B in the equation

$$T_B \;=\; (P_B/P_M)\,273.15,$$

where P_B and P_M signify the measured gas pressure at the boiling point of water and at the melting point of ice. We might of course simply choose some one real gas as *the* (standard) thermometric fluid, but such a procedure would be an arbitrary expression of human choice, seriously impairing the absoluteness we would wish to impute to our temperature scale. However, this disagreeable expedient can easily be avoided. Knowing that real gases approach ideal behavior as their pressures approach zero, we have only to make (for each real gas that comes in question) a series of measurements of the *ratio* P_B/P_M when various progressively decreasing quantities of gas are present in the system.† For *each* gas we then extrapo-

---

* Strictly speaking, we assign 273.16°K to the "triple point" at which ice, water, and water vapor coexist at equilibrium in the absence of air.
† As $P \to 0$, the individual values of P_B and P_M must also approach zero, but their ratio remains finite.

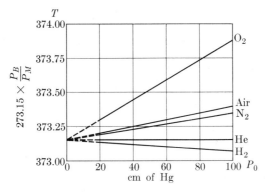

Figure 2–15

late the various measured ratios P_B/P_M to zero pressure, taking this extrapolated value as the pressure ratio that would be shown by an ideal gas at all pressures. We expect that *all* real gases should yield the *same* limiting (ideal) value for the ratio P_B/P_M and, as Fig. 2–15 shows, this is precisely what we do find. Thus, though we use only real gases, we can still constitute what we call an ideal-gas temperature scale—simply by applying Amontons' law only to extrapolated (ideal) values. That is, to establish the value of *any* temperature (T), we establish the limiting value of the ratio P_T/P_M, and then substitute in the equation

$$T = \lim_{P \to 0} P_T/P_M \cdot 273.15.$$

And ultimately one can show, by thermodynamic analysis, that the scale of temperatures thus constituted does, indeed, represent an *absolute* scale.

Atomic weights from limiting densities. We asked how we could use Avogadro's rule to obtain *accurate* values for relative atomic weights from gas-density data for real gases, to which the rule is only *approximately* applicable. The answer now is clear: we must somehow extrapolate our actual density data to find the limiting (ideal) values to which Avogadro's rule applies rigorously. The particular extrapolation required here is not far to seek. For an ideal gas we write

$$PV = nRT.$$

Multiplying both sides by the molecular weight (M) of the gas in question, and dividing through by PV, we find

$$M = \frac{1}{P} \frac{nM}{V} RT.$$

What does the quotient nM/V represent? The numerator is the number of moles of gas times its molecular weight, hence, the total weight of gas present. The denominator is the total volume of the gas. Therefore, the quotient is simply the number of grams of gas per unit volume, i.e. its density (δ), and we have

$$M = (\delta/P)\, RT.$$

For a given ideal gas at a given temperature, the ratio δ/P is invariant,* but for a real gas this need not be the case. By submitting the real gas to a series of density measurements, at constant temperature but progressively diminishing pressures, we obtain values for the ratio δ/P which

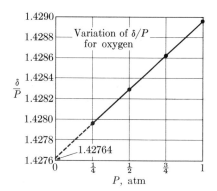

Figure 2–16

can be plotted as shown in Fig. 2–16. As $P \to 0$, so also does $\delta \to 0$, but the *ratio δ/P remains finite* and, in the limit of $P = 0$, we establish the limiting value that would be shown by an ideal gas. Substituting this limiting value in the last equation, we can then calculate an accurate molecular weight for the gas. If the gas is an element, and we have previously determined (from combining-volume data) the formula of its gaseous particle, we are then at once able to establish its atomic weight.†

We have now made a considerable advance. For the elements hydrogen, oxygen, nitrogen, chlorine, and the few others we have so far been able to treat, we have developed two distinct methods of establishing atomic weights. The first uses *combining-volume* data, interpreted with the aid of Avogadro's rule applied as an approximation, to establish the formulas of such compounds as H_2O—which formulas we apply to draw from accurate *combining-weight* data accurate values for relative atomic weights. The second method uses the same *combining-volume* data, interpreted in terms of Avogadro's rule applied only as an approximation, to determine the formulas of the gaseous particles of the elements, for example H_2, O_2, etc.—which formulas we apply in the calculation of accurate relative atomic weights obtained by making a rigorous application of Avogadro's rule to

---

* Consider that when the pressure on a certain mass of ideal gas is halved, its volume is doubled. Inasmuch as the mass of gas is then spread over twice as large a volume, its density is also halved—i.e., the ratio δ/P is independent of pressure.

† If it is not at once apparent how Avogadro's rule enters this calculation, consider how we obtained a numerical value for R (see p. 65). The value of R was based on a numerical value for the molar volume, which will be the same for all gases only if Avogadro's rule applies rigorously to all gases in the limit $P \to 0$. Thus when, in the above method, we use a unique value of R in the determination of the molecular weights of various gases, there is in fact an invocation of Avogadro's rule which, if only implicit, is nonetheless essential.

values extrapolated from *gas-density* data. The excellent agreement of the results obtained by both methods is an extremely heartening indication that we are on the right track. Yet there are still two points that leave much to be desired.

First: Both our methods depend alike on the same interpretation of certain combining-volume data. The agreement of the results obtained does not then preclude the possibility of error in these data or these interpretations. If we seek full confirmation of our results, we must seek still other methods for obtaining atomic weights that are independent of those data and interpretations.

Second: The methods so far in hand apply only to a small number of gaseous or readily volatile elements. To complete the foundations of our atomic theory we must then seek other methods for obtaining atomic weights that are applicable to *all* elements. Both these quests are pushed to a successful conclusion in the next chapter.

Illustrative Examples

Caveat: In these examples, and in the succeeding problems, we are still assuming the availability of data we have yet to show attainable.

Illustrative Example. When metallic hafnium (symbol Hf; atomic weight, 179) reacts with hot hydrogen chloride (HCl), the reaction of 3.58 gm of hafnium is accompanied by the release of 448 ml of gaseous hydrogen (H_2) measured at 136.5°C and 3 atm pressure. Calculate the moles of hydrogen liberated per gram-atom of hafnium reacted, and write a balanced equation for the reaction.

An obvious first step in solving this problem is the calculation of the STP volume of hydrogen released. This calculation is easily carried out with the aid of the combined form of Boyle's and Charles' laws:

$$\frac{P_1 V_1}{T_1} = \frac{P_2 V_2}{T_2}, \qquad V_1 = V_2 \frac{P_2}{P_1} \frac{T_1}{T_2}.$$

Take the subscript $_1$ to represent the values under STP conditions (1 atm, 273°K), and the subscript $_2$ to denote the values under the experimental conditions. On making appropriate substitutions in the last equation, we find that

$$V_1 = 448 \times \frac{3}{1} \times \frac{273}{273 + 136.5}$$

$$= 448 \times 3 \times \frac{2}{3}$$

$$= 896 \text{ ml STP.}$$

And then the number of moles of hydrogen present $= \dfrac{896}{22400} = 0.04.$

There is nothing wrong with this familiar mode of calculation, but see how much more easily the same result is obtained by use of the equation $PV = nRT$. Taking care to express pressure and volume in cm Hg and liters, respectively, we use 6.23 for the value of R and write

$$(3 \cdot 76)(0.448) = n(6.23)(409.5),$$

$$n = 0.04 \text{ mole.}$$

We are asked not for the number of moles of hydrogen actually released but for the number of moles that would be released by one gram-atom of hafnium. How many gram-atoms of hafnium have figured in our experiment?

$$\text{gram-atoms of Hf} = \frac{\text{grams Hf}}{\text{atomic weight Hf}} = \frac{3.58}{179} = 0.02.$$

Knowing that 0.02 gram-atom of hafnium releases 0.04 mole of hydrogen, we see that 2 moles of hydrogen would be released by 1 gram-atom of hafnium. Thus the answer to the first part of the question is 2. By the converse of the MOP we may conclude that if 2 moles of hydrogen are liberated by 1 gram-atom of hafnium, then 2 molecules of hydrogen must be released by each atom of hafnium, as is shown in the skeleton equation

$$\text{Hf} + \qquad \rightarrow 2\text{H}_2 + \qquad .$$

To the left side of the equation we must add the hydrogen chloride from which hydrogen is liberated by the hafnium. Four formula-units of HCl will be required to furnish the 4 atoms (2 molecules) of hydrogen appearing on the right-hand side of the equation. Thus we will write

$$\text{Hf} + 4 \text{ HCl} \rightarrow 2 \text{ H}_2 + \qquad .$$

What else is to be added? We have still to dispose of 1 hafnium atom and 4 chlorine atoms, which appear on the left but not on the right in the last equation. *Assuming* that the product is a simple chloride of hafnium, it is tempting to assign HfCl$_4$ as the formula of that chloride, and to write:

$$\text{Hf} + 4 \text{ HCl} \rightarrow 2 \text{ H}_2 + \text{HfCl}_4.$$

Illustrative Example. At elevated temperatures sulfur nitride (S_4N_4) decomposes explosively into nitrogen (N_2) and sulfur vapor. It is found that under CTP conditions, 2.5 volumes of gaseous products are formed for each 1.0 volume of sulfur nitride decomposed. Write a balanced equation for the decomposition reaction.

More explicit information about the individual volumes of the product gases is obviously desirable. We observe that each molecule of S_4N_4 contains four atoms of nitrogen. From each molecule of S_4N_4 we will then obtain two molecules of nitrogen, N_2. Knowing that one molecule of S_4N_4 gives rise to two molecules of N_2, we can use Avogadro's rule to draw the inference that 2.0 volumes of gaseous N_2 will be produced from 1.0 volume of S_4N_4. Hence, of the 2.5 volumes of gaseous products obtained in the decomposition of 1 volume of S_4N_4, only $(2.5 - 2.0)$ or 0.5 volume of sulfur vapor is obtained. Since the volume of the sulfur vapor obtained is only one-half the volume of S_4N_4 used, it is indicated that from one molecule of S_4N_4 there is obtained only one-half molecule of sulfur vapor. Each molecule of S_4N_4 contains four sulfur atoms, and these appear to constitute but one-half of one molecule of sulfur vapor. Thus the molecule of sulfur vapor must contain *eight* sulfur atoms, and we write

$$S_4N_4 \rightarrow 2\,N_2 + \tfrac{1}{2}\,S_8,$$

or

$$2\,S_4N_4 \rightarrow 4\,N_2 + S_8.$$

Illustrative Example. When the gaseous hydrocarbon ethane is burned in oxygen, the gas volumes measured under CTP conditions are

2 volumes ethane $+$ 7 volumes O_2
$$\rightarrow 6 \text{ volumes } H_2O \text{ (gas) } + 4 \text{ volumes } CO_2.$$

Determine the molecular formula of ethane.

Given Avogadro's rule, anything that can be said about relative CTP gas volumes can be said also about relative numbers of gas molecules. Hence we write

$$2 \text{ ethane } + 7\,O_2 \rightarrow 6\,H_2O + 4\,CO_2.$$

All the hydrogen and carbon appearing on the right must come from the ethane, which, as a hydrocarbon, is known to contain *only* carbon and hydrogen. On the right we have 12 atoms of hydrogen and 4 atoms of carbon, all of which come from 2 molecules of ethane. Hence the molecular formula of ethane is C_2H_6.

Illustrative Example. A certain gaseous hydrocarbon is known to contain less than 5 carbon atoms. This compound was burned with exactly the volume of oxygen (O_2) required for complete combustion. The total volume of the reactants, all being gaseous, was 600 ml. The total volume of the products (CO_2 and H_2O vapor) under the same conditions of temperature and pressure was 700 ml. What is the formula of the hydrocarbon?

Effectively, we are given only the $6:7$ *ratio* of the total volume of the reactants (the hydrocarbon and O_2) to the total volume of the products (H_2O and CO_2). What can be done with this apparently quite inadequate datum? Knowing nothing about the formula of the compound, let us begin boldly by assigning to it the general formula C_xH_y, where x and y are integral but unknown. Let us then formulate a skeleton equation:

$$C_xH_y + O_2 \rightarrow CO_2 + H_2O.$$

Each molecule of the hydrocarbon contains x atoms of carbon, each molecule of CO_2 contains one atom of carbon. Therefore, x molecules of CO_2 should be obtained from each molecule of the hydrocarbon. Our equation then becomes

$$C_xH_y + O_2 \rightarrow x\,CO_2 + H_2O.$$

Each molecule of the hydrocarbon contains y hydrogen atoms, which will suffice for the formation of $y/2$ molecules of water vapor, each containing two atoms of hydrogen. Hence

$$C_xH_y + O_2 \rightarrow x\,CO_2 + \frac{y}{2}\,H_2O.$$

The total number of atoms of oxygen on the right of the equation is $(2x + y/2)$. Each molecule of oxygen containing two oxygen atoms, there will be only half as many molecules of oxygen required as there are atoms of oxygen on the right. The number of molecules of O_2 required is then $(x + y/4)$, so that

$$C_xH_y + \left(x + \frac{y}{4}\right)O_2 \rightarrow xCO_2 + \frac{y}{2}\,H_2O.$$

Since all measurements were made under CTP conditions, this equation may be taken to signify that 1 volume of the hydrocarbon C_xH_y reacts with $(x + y/4)$ volumes of O_2 to give x volumes of CO_2 and $y/2$ volumes of H_2O vapor. Therefore

$$\text{total volume of reactants } (C_xH_y + O_2) = 1 + x + y/4,$$

$$\text{total volume of products } (CO_2 + H_2O) = x + y/2.$$

We are told that these two total volumes stand in the ratio of 6 to 7. Therefore

$$\frac{1 + x + y/4}{x + y/2} = \frac{6}{7}, \qquad 7 + 7x + \frac{7}{4}y = 6x + 3y,$$

$$7 + x = \frac{5}{4}y, \qquad \frac{28 + 4x}{5} = y.$$

This looks pretty hopeless: one equation in two unknowns. But we still have some information in reserve: we know that both x *and* y *are positive integers,* and that x *is less than 5.* We can try to solve the above equation uniquely by substituting the values 1, 2, 3, and 4 for x, thereby establishing which value of x corresponds to an integral value for y. The only integral solution for y is obtained when $x = 3$:

$$y = \frac{28 + 4(3)}{5} = \frac{40}{5} = 8.$$

Thus the formula for the hydrocarbon must be C_3H_8, and the equation of the reaction is

$$C_3H_8 + 5\,O_2 = 3\,CO_2 + 4\,H_2O.$$

PROBLEMS

1. A tank contains oxygen gas at an absolute pressure of 2000 lb/in². On the withdrawal of 5 ft³ of oxygen, measured at atmospheric pressure (14.7 lb/in²), the pressure in the tank is observed to fall to 1934 lb/in². Assuming that there is no net change in the temperature of the gas, calculate the volume, in cubic feet, of the tank.

2. At a pressure of 76.0 cm Hg and a temperature of 27°C the density of hydrogen is 0.08 gm/liter. Calculate the average velocity of the hydrogen molecule at this temperature. *Note:* in this calculation you must take care to use homogeneous units. If, taking the density of mercury as 13.5 gm/cm³, you propose to use the units cm-gm-sec, then you should express the pressure in dynes/cm² (1 gram-force = 980 dynes) and the density in gm/cm³. The calculated velocity will then be in cm/sec.

3. A gaseous compound containing only nitrogen and hydrogen is found to contain 12.3% by weight of hydrogen. Relative to the density of air taken as unity (in the style of Gay-Lussac), the density of hydrogen is 0.069, that of nitrogen is 0.996, and that of the compound is 1.103. Making no assumptions about the formulas of any of these species, calculate the number of volumes of hydrogen and of nitrogen that combine to form one volume of the compound. Do the results conform to Gay-Lussac's law?

4. A compound containing only C, N, and H is burned with oxygen under such conditions that the individual volumes of the reactants and products can be measured at the same temperature and pressure. It is then found that 4 volumes of the compound react with oxygen to yield 4 volumes of CO_2, 4 volumes of NO, and 10 volumes of H_2O (vapor).

   (a) What volume of oxygen is required for the combustion? Could you calculate, from the data given, the weight of the oxygen? Explain!

   (b) What is the formula of the unknown compound? Is this an empirical or a molecular formula?

   (c) Taking 22.4 liter STP as the gram-molecular volume and 18 as the molecular weight of water, calculate how many grams of water would be obtained when 2.24 liters STP of the compound are burned.

5. A gaseous compound known to contain only carbon, sulfur, and hydrogen is mixed with exactly the volume of gaseous O_2 required for the complete combustion of the compound to CO_2, SO_2, and H_2O. On burning 11 volumes of the gaseous *mixture*, there are produced 4 volumes of CO_2, 6 volumes of gaseous H_2O, and 2 volumes of SO_2, all measurements being made under the same conditions of temperature and pressure.

   (a) How many volumes of oxygen are required for the combustion?

   (b) What is the molecular formula of the compound?

6. On strong heating, both $KClO_3$ and $KClO_4$ are completely decomposed to KCl and O_2 gas. In the course of analysis of a mixture of $KClO_3$ and $KClO_4$, it is found that the complete decomposition of a 1-gm sample of the mixture results in the liberation of exactly 300 ml STP of gaseous oxygen. Set up a completely numerical equation from which the percentage of

$KClO_3$ in the mixture can be calculated. (Atomic weights: O, 16; Cl, 35.5; K, 39. Molar volume: 22.4 liters STP.)

7. The molecular equations for the reaction of metallic aluminum and zinc with hydrochloric acid are, respectively, $2 Al + 6 HCl \rightarrow 2 AlCl_3 + 3 H_2$ and $Zn + 2 HCl \rightarrow ZnCl_2 + H_2$. In the analysis of an aluminum-zinc alloy, it is found that the solution of 0.100 gm of alloy in excess dilute hydrochloric acid produces 91.5 ml of gaseous H_2 measured over the solution (vapor pressure = 24 mm Hg) at 298°K and 750 mm Hg pressure. Given 27.0 and 65.4 as the atomic weights of aluminum and zinc respectively, calculate the weight percent of aluminum in the alloy.

8. (a) At 0°C actual measurements of the density of gaseous ammonia yield the results shown in Table 2–3. Determine the limiting density of ammonia and, taking $R = 0.082054$ liter-atm/mole-°K, calculate the accurate molecular weight of ammonia, NH_3.

TABLE 2–3

Pressure, atm	1	$\frac{2}{3}$	$\frac{1}{2}$	$\frac{1}{3}$
Density, gm/liter	0.77169	0.51182	0.38293	0.25461

(b) In ammonia 4.6319 gm of nitrogen unites with each 1.0000 gm of hydrogen present. Using the result obtained in (a), determine the accurate atomic weights of nitrogen *and* hydrogen.

9. (a) Given 22.414 liters as the STP molar volume of an ideal gas, calculate the value of the gas-law-constant R in the units ml-atm/mole-°K.

(b) Given that a pressure of 1 atm represents a force of 1.013×10^6 dynes/cm², use the answer obtained in part (a) to determine that $R = 8.31$ joules/mole-°K.

(c) A sample of helium exerts a pressure of 3 atm in a 2-liter vessel held at 27°C; a sample of neon exerts a pressure of 4 atm in a 3-liter vessel held at 127°C. While carefully maintaining the two vessels at their original temperatures, we open a valve between them so that the two gas samples can form a homogeneous mixture. What will be the total pressure exerted by this mixture?

10. (a) To 10 ml of a pure gaseous hydrocarbon is added 90 ml of pure oxygen (O_2). The passage of a spark through this mixture produces an explosion in which the hydrocarbon is completely oxidized to gaseous CO_2, and to liquid H_2O which (for the purposes of this analysis) may be regarded as essentially involatile. Hence, the 65 ml of residual gas measured after the explosion contains only CO_2 and excess O_2. Assuming all volumetric measurements made under CTP conditions, to what extent do the given data permit you to define the formula of the hydrocarbon?

(b) To 10 ml of a gaseous mixture, containing only CH_4 and C_2H_6, is added 90 ml of pure oxygen (O_2). The passage of a spark through this mixture produces an explosion in which the hydrocarbon is completely oxidized to gaseous CO_2, and to liquid H_2O which (for the purposes of this analysis) may be regarded as essentially involatile. Hence, the 76 ml of residual gas measured after the explosion contains only CO_2 and excess O_2. Assuming all volumetric measurements made under CTP conditions, determine the composition of the original hydrocarbon mixture.

11. Henry's law refers to the solubility of a given gas in a given liquid at a given temperature.

(a) Two statements of the law are:
   (i) the *volume* of gas dissolved by 1 volume of liquid is *independent* of the pressure;
   (ii) the *weight* of gas dissolved by 1 volume of liquid is *directly proportional* to the pressure.

   Show that these two statements are entirely equivalent for an ideal gas.

(b) When equilibrium is reached between the gas and its solution, we may imagine that, per unit time, the number of gas particles entering and the number of gas particles leaving the solution must be equal. Taking care to make your assumptions explicit, sketch a line of argument that would permit one to derive Henry's law from the kinetic-molecular view.

(c) At reasonably low pressures, the volume of a given gas that is dissolved by unit volume of a given liquid is independent of the presence or absence of other gases in mixture with the gas in question. On the basis of this observation, and using the interpretation of Henry's law proposed in (b), show how one might construct an argument for belief in the universality of the Boltzmann constant k.

12. Nothing about our statement of Graham's law excludes its application to the same gas at different temperatures.

(a) For the same gas measured at $273°K$ and $1092°K$, and under the same (low) pressure, calculate
   (i) the ratio of the two measured densities,
   (ii) the ratio of the average particle velocities, and
   (iii) the ratio of the numbers of gas particles present per unit volume at the two temperatures.

(b) If we consider the ratio of the numbers of gas particles reaching (and passing through) the orifice area in unit time at the two temperatures, surely that ratio must depend on both ratios (ii) and (iii) above. Why? If, as we have done, we consider only the ratio of the volume losses *measured under the actual working pressure*, then only ratio (ii) need be taken into account. Why?

(c) Compared with ours, the usual statement of Graham's law is more restrictive in that it stipulates constancy of *both* temperature and pressure, but more general in that it refers to effusion rates that may be measured under the working pressure, *or* under STP conditions, etc. Explain the relation between the elements of restrictiveness and generality.

THE SYSTEMATIC ASSIGNMENT OF ATOMIC WEIGHTS

Consider the specifications of the method(s) we must seek to complete our assignment of atomic weights. The experimental measurements required for a determination of limiting gas densities are both tedious and extremely demanding. We seek methods that do not call on any such determinations, in which case accurate relative atomic weights will have to be calculated from combining-weight data. This is no drawback: combining-weight data are among those most readily accessible experimentally. But to draw relative atomic weights from combining-weight data we must, as noted in Chapter 1, be able to establish the formulas of the compounds to which these data refer. Moreover, in establishing these formulas, we must find some substitute for the combining-volume method used in Chapter 2. That method is effective, we saw, only as applied to the small number of gaseous or readily gasifiable elements. Thus we can pinpoint our problem: what general method(s) can we develop for assigning formulas to compounds?

The first method we will consider still pivots on the use of gas-density data. Though only about 10% of the elements are themselves gaseous or readily volatile, some 35% form a substantial variety of gaseous compounds. Carbon, for example, boils above 4000°K, but forms a great variety of compounds that can be handled as gases at, or only slightly above, room temperature. By a systematic study of the vapor densities of such compounds, we can establish their formulas. Before examining the details of this method, we should say something of the gas-density data the method demands. These densities are ordinarily measured at only one finite pressure, and no extrapolation to limiting densities is then possible. Hence, Avogadro's rule is applicable only as an approximation in the interpretation of these data. This poses no real difficulty: that rule is involved only in the derivation of formulas, and not at all in the subsequent use of these formulas to draw accurate atomic weights from combining-weight data. In such circumstances the approximateness of the rule can be made good, as we saw in the last chapter, by imposing the boundary condition that the formulas must involve only comparatively *small whole numbers*. Moreover, given the power of this boundary restriction, it is (or will soon become) quite clear that we need only *approximate* gas-density data—inasmuch as Avogadro's rule will be applicable *only* as an approximation, whether or not the gas-density data themselves are exact.

Determination of Vapor Densities

Implementation of the method sketched above presupposes the availability of simple experimental techniques that can furnish a large number of approximate gas-density data. Many of the compounds with which we must work are vaporizable only at temperatures above room temperature, and are often highly reactive at these temperatures. The Regnault gas-density method noted in the last chapter is inapplicable to high-temperature work with reactive vapors. The stopcock is the vulnerable point: even if we use a stopcock lubricant stiff enough to resist melting at high temperatures, that lubricant will often prove susceptible to attack by the vapors under study and/or capable of dissolving substantial quantities of them. We must then consider the availability of simple but reliable vapor-density methods not vulnerable in this (or other) respects. Three such methods will now be described.

The Hofmann method. We use an ordinary barometer tube that has been graduated to show the free volume between the closed end and the mercury level in the tube, wherever that level may stand. We jacket the tube as shown in Fig. 3–1. Filling the tube with mercury, we invert it in a bowl of mercury to set it up as a barometer, with the free space at the top void, that is, a Torricellian vacuum. We heat the jacket—to 100°C by passing through it steam from a water boiler, to higher temperatures (if these are necessary to vaporize the substance) by putting into the boiler some liquid whose boiling point is higher than that of water. While the system is coming to equilibrium, we introduce the sample to be studied into a tiny vial fitted with an unlubricated ground-glass stopper. The vial is made very small

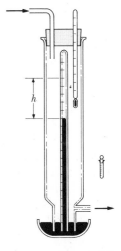

Figure 3–1

so that it can be slipped into the bottom of the barometer. It is also made very small so that it may be completely filled with liquid—in order that no air may be carried into the system by this route—without using more of the sample than can be vaporized in the limited volume available at the top of the barometer tube.* By weighing the vial empty and after it is filled, we determine the weight of the sample taken for study. We then slip the vial under the surface of the mercury in the bowl, and we release it under the mouth of the barometer tube whence, given the high density of mercury, it floats to the mercury surface within the barometer. The rapid vaporization of the sample in this hot (and initially vacuous) region ordinarily blows out the stopper of the vial. But even if the stopper is not thus displaced, the vapor will pass quite rapidly around the unlubricated ground stopper into the barometer tube. As the sample vaporizes, the gas pressure now exerted within the barometer produces a fall of the mercury level within the tube. When the level has again become stationary, the volume occupied by the vapor (V) is read off from the graduations of the tube. The pressure of the vapor (P) can be equated to the difference in height (h) between the original and the final mercury levels in the barometer, since the pressure of the vapor is uniquely responsible for the depression of the mercury level.† The temperature of the vapor (T) is the readily measurable temperature prevailing inside the jacket. Knowing the weight (w) of the sample used, the STP density of the vapor is now easily calculated as follows:

$$V_{STP} = V \frac{273}{T} \frac{P}{760},$$

$$\delta_{STP} = \frac{w}{V_{STP}} = \frac{w}{V} \frac{T}{273} \frac{760}{P}.$$

An even simpler and more direct calculation, yielding at once the *approximate molecular weight* of the vapor, proceeds by way of the equation

$$M = \frac{\delta}{P} RT = \frac{w}{PV} RT.$$

Results good to about 5% are readily obtained. The method suffers, however, from limitations imposed by the necessary use of mercury. It is

---

* If the sample is a solid, it must be melted before it is introduced into the vial, to exclude the air that would otherwise be introduced in the crevices between the grains or lumps of solid. Once the vial has been charged in this fashion, the melted material may be allowed to solidify *in situ*.

† A (small) correction should be made for the fact that at the elevated temperature within the jacket, the density of mercury is slightly less than at room temperature.

inapplicable to vapors that attack mercury, and to materials that can be vaporized only at temperatures approaching the boiling point of mercury. These limitations are removed in the following two methods, neither of which requires use of mercury.

The Dumas method. Imagine a glass bulb with a long slender neck bent as shown in Fig. 3–2. The bulb is weighed while open to the air. It is then charged with the sample under consideration by slightly warming the bulb, then permitting it to cool with its open tip under the surface of the liquid (or molten solid) sample. Repeating this process as required, we charge the bulb (ordinarily about 250 ml in volume) with several grams of sample. This is a huge excess over the quantity of sample required to fill the bulb with vapor. We now immerse the bulb as shown, and heat the bath to some temperature above the boiling point of the sample. As the sample boils away, its vapor progressively sweeps all the air out of the flask. When at last equilibrium is reached, as indicated by the cessation of all gas flow from the tip of the flask, we can be sure that the vessel is filled with sample vapor at the prevailing pressure of the atmosphere and the temperature of the bath. We then at once apply a small flame to seal the tip of the flask. Removing the flask from the bath, we cool it and weigh it for a second time. Having scratched the capillary neck with a

file, we immerse the flask in a large volume of water, and break off the capillary tip under water. The water rushes in to fill the flask. (Why?) From the fact that water now fills the flask essentially completely, we gain assurance that all air *was* swept from the flask by the excess sample vapor. We conclude the experiment by making a third weighing, in which the flask, filled with water, is weighed together with the fragment of the neck we broke off in order to fill it.

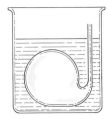

Figure 3–2

From the difference of the third and second weighings we obtain the weight of water required to fill the flask, the volume occupied by the *condensed* sample being negligible. Knowing the density of water, we can thus establish the volume (V) of the flask. From the difference of the second and first weighings we obtain the difference in the weight of the *vapor* that filled the volume V at temperature T and atmospheric pressure, and the weight of *air* that initially filled volume V at room temperature and atmospheric pressure. But Regnault-style experiments inform us of the density of air under these conditions, so that we can easily establish the weight of air (w_a) present initially. We can then calculate the weight (w) of the vapor sample from the equation

$$w - w_a = \text{weight } 2 - \text{weight } 1.$$

Knowing w and V, the barometric pressure (P), and the bath temperature (T), we can as before readily calculate the vapor density and molecular weight of the sample.

The Victor Meyer method. The Dumas method requires a comparatively large sample (if only to sweep the air out of the flask), constant reconstruction of the experimental vessel, a good many separate operations consuming a good deal of time. Moreover, that method is wholly inapplicable to materials that boil at or above the softening point of glass. All such limitations are absent from the Victor Meyer method, which employs the apparatus shown in Fig. 3–3. For high-temperature work the lower part of the inner tube may be made of a high-melting material like glazed porcelain, and the outer tube may be replaced by a furnace. Let us, however, discuss only the simpler case, in which a temperature of 100°C is amply high. We can then charge the outer jacket with water which, when boiled, will maintain the inner assembly at 100°C. (It is not necessary that the apparatus be at exactly the *same* temperature throughout its considerable height, but it is essential that the temperature profile, whatever it is, be *steady.*) The inner tube bears at its lower end a pear-shaped bulb, and at its upper end (which stands at room temperature) it is fitted with the indicated connections. A minute vial, charged with the sample, is inserted at the top, where it remains (as shown) suspended on a glass rod. The assembled apparatus is then heated and, when no more air bubbles emerge

from the delivery tip (i.e. when the system has reached a steady temperature), an inverted graduate filled with water is set above the delivery tube as shown. By a slight withdrawal of the glass rod, through its rubber sleeve, the vial is now freed to fall into the lower bulb, where a small amount of glass wool or sand may be placed to cushion its fall. The sample is vaporized in the bulbous region, whence it diffuses only slowly because it is ordinarily much denser than air. Provided that we have made the inner tube sufficiently long (18 in. is ordinarily ample), the vapor will not be able to reach any region cool enough to permit its condensation. We can then feel confident that *all* the sample is in the vapor state at the time we make our measurements.

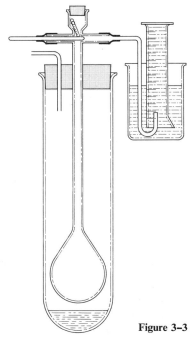

Figure 3–3

In consequence of the vaporization of the sample, a certain quantity of air will be expelled from the delivery tube into the graduate where—when all gas flow has ceased—the volume of gas collected is measured at room temperature and atmospheric pressure. Making the appropriate correction for the admixture of the expelled air with water vapor in the graduate, one can then calculate the STP volume of air expelled by the formation of the vapor. The partial pressure of the vapor is not only unknown but certainly variable at different altitudes within the inner tube. Moreover, the temperature may vary from one such altitude to another. It is then a fact at once surprising and delightful that the STP volume of dry air expelled into the graduate is also precisely the volume the weighed sample would fill were it gaseous under STP conditions.* Knowing the vapor volume of a weighed sample under STP conditions, we can proceed as before to calculate the STP vapor density and the molecular weight of the sample. The entire experiment can be carried through in $\frac{1}{2}$ hour and yields results good to a few percent.

The Cannizzaro Relationship

Assured that the approximate vapor-density data we need are accessible, we now turn to the simple relation on which Cannizzaro founded a method for establishing the atomic weights of elements that—though not gaseous or readily volatile themselves—form a considerable number of volatile compounds. To make sure that the results yielded by this method are concordant with those earlier obtained by use of combining-volume data, we begin by applying Cannizzaro's method to a gaseous element, nitrogen. Consider the data in Table 3–1. The first column of figures contains the measured STP densities for all the substances listed. The second column contains the results of analytic determinations of the fraction by weight of nitrogen in each substance. Multiplying together the paired figures in the first and second columns, we obtain the results given in the third, which represent the weights of nitrogen present in unit volume of each of the indicated substances. The ratios of these weights, displayed in the

---

* At the beginning of the experiment the inner tube contained some unknown number of moles of air (n_a). At the end of the experiment a measurable number of moles of air (n_e) have been expelled into the graduate, and the inner tube must then contain $(n_a - n_e)$ moles of air plus the n_x moles of vaporous sample. However, if the pressure and the temperature profile in the inner tube remain at the end as they were at the beginning, the total number of moles of gas in the inner tube must remain unchanged. Therefore we can write $(n_a - n_e) + n_x = n_a$, whence it follows that $n_x = n_e$. That is, the number of moles of air expelled into the graduate is equal to the number of moles of sample vaporized in the inner tube. Avogadro's rule entails the equality of all STP molar volumes. Hence, the STP volume of the dry air expelled is just the volume that would be occupied by the sample were it vaporous under STP conditions. (Q.E.D.)

TABLE 3–1

Substance	STP densities, gm/liter	Weight fraction of nitrogen in substance, wt% N/100	Grams of nitrogen in 1 liter STP	Ratios of weights in preceding column	Formulas inferred from the ratios
Nitrogen	1.251	1.00	1.251	2	N_2
Nitric oxide	1.340	0.466	0.625	1	$N_1O?$
Nitrous oxide	1.978	0.636	1.258	2	$N_2O?$
Ammonia	0.771	0.823	0.634	1	$N_1H?$
Hydrazine	1.42	0.874	1.24	2	$N_2H?$
Cyanogen	2.38	0.538	1.28	2	$N_2C?$
Methylamine	1.40	0.451	0.63	1	$N_1C?H?$

fourth column, manifest the strikingly simple regularity that is the focus of Cannizzaro's method. That is, the ratios of the numbers in the third column represent a remarkably close approach to the *small whole numbers* shown in the fourth. Were we to extend our listing to include more exotic compounds, we would find some larger numbers in the fourth column. But no matter *how* far we extend our table, we never find weights in the third column that are related to the other weights therein by anything but a close approximation to a ratio of small whole numbers. In what terms shall we explain this empirical finding?

We are concerned with 1 liter STP of each of the substances. To the extent that Avogadro's rule applies to real gases, we are then dealing with approximately equal numbers of molecules of each substance. The weights of nitrogen tabulated in the third column thus represent the weights of nitrogen present in approximately the *same* number (η) of molecules of each substance. Now should there not be a simple relation among those weights? A given compound may contain 1 atom of nitrogen per molecule— or 2, or 3, or 4 atoms of nitrogen per molecule—but we have good reason to believe that these numbers are *always* comparatively small whole numbers. Therefore, to the degree of approximation with which Avogadro's rule applies to real gases, the *numbers* of nitrogen atoms present in 1 liter STP of each substance must be η, 2η, 3η, etc. The *weights* of nitrogen present must then stand in the same small-whole-number ratios.* The weights actually observed *do* approach just such ratios to well within the margin of uncertainty left by Avogadro's rule. Thus we find that the empirical regularity is readily explicable—only to be expected. And, assured now of its genuineness, let us seek to turn it to account.

---

* *Here* is the boundary condition tacitly invoked when we rounded off the ratios of weights in the third column to obtain the small whole numbers entered in the fourth.

All the numbers in the third column stand very close to integral multiples of 0.625. And even when we examine very many stable nitrogen compounds, and thus extend the table we have given over several pages, we never find a third-column entry less than 0.625. To what does that number correspond? If we have studied a sufficient range of nitrogen compounds, it is surely reasonable to expect that we must somewhere encounter a compound that contains but one nitrogen atom per molecule. To that compound should correspond the minimum weight of nitrogen per liter of compound. A compound containing twice this minimum weight may be presumed to contain two atoms of nitrogen per molecule, and so on. Hence, the data in our table permit us to write provisionally the partial formulas appearing in its last column. *Only provisionally* because, however many nitrogen compounds we have studied, it remains conceivable that a number like 0.625/2 will make its appearance in the third column of the table when some yet unexamined compound is brought under study. Can we then afford to discount the possibility that experimental data will some time demand in practice the kind of revision we see as conceivable in principle?

Recall our earlier use of combining-volume data to establish such formulas as H_2, O_2, N_2, etc. (see p. 57). There we had to make the assumption that, if we study a sufficient variety of gaseous compounds of a given gaseous element, we must sooner or later encounter one such compound containing a single atom of the element per molecule. Clearly this is no different from the assumption made in the preceding paragraph. However, this assumption, perfectly plausible in itself, need not *now* be made in so extreme a form. Suppose, for example, that we were concerned with discounting the possibility that the weight 0.625 gm of nitrogen corresponds in fact to a compound containing *two* atoms of nitrogen per molecule. We need not build all our hopes on the chance that we will encounter a compound that (containing *one* atom of nitrogen per molecule) introduces the figure 0.625/2 into the third column. All we need actually assume is that, if we study a sufficient variety of nitrogen compounds, we will sooner or later encounter one that contains an *odd* number (z) of atoms of nitrogen per molecule. For the error of our provisional assignment would then be unequivocally signified by the appearance in the third column of the figure ($z \times 0.625/2$), which is a *nonintegral* multiple of 0.625. Having studied a great variety of stable nitrogen compounds without once having encountered any such occasion for revision, surely we have considerable basis for confidence in the partial formulas assigned in the last column of our table.

Subject only to the validity of this eminently plausible supplementary assumption, the formula of gaseous nitrogen is established as N_2, confirming the earlier finding we based on combining-volume data. And we may then think to conclude our determination of the atomic weight of nitrogen as follows.   Multiplying the measured density of nitrogen (1.25 gm/liter) by 22.4, we find the weight of a mole of gaseous nitrogen, that is, $(1.25)(22.4) = 28$.   Given knowledge that the gaseous molecule of nitrogen contains two atoms, the atomic weight of nitrogen is thus established as 14.   In point of principle, this calculation leaves a *great* deal to be desired.   For one thing, it applies, to the density of a real gas measured at 1 atm pressure, the figure 22.4 which applies rigorously only to an ideal gas.   Short of a difficult determination of limiting density, this method cannot supply an accurate value for the atomic weight of nitrogen.   As a second shortcoming, note that by thus introducing the figure 22.4, we throw away the possibility of founding on Cannizzaro's method a determination of atomic weights that is completely independent of all our earlier conclusions founded on combining-volume data.   This important possibility can easily be realized if only we defer our effort to establish the atomic weight of nitrogen until after we have examined one more set of tabulated data.

Let us prepare for the element carbon, our reference standard of atomic weight, a table like that already prepared for nitrogen.   Recall that, unlike nitrogen, the involatile element carbon could not at all be studied by combining-volume methods.   However, finding that carbon forms a great variety of volatile compounds, we can readily subject it to exactly the same kind of analysis just carried through with nitrogen.   The numbers shown in the fourth column of Table 3–2 are of greater diversity than those appearing in the nitrogen table, and reach higher values—reflecting the greater molecular complexity of carbon compounds.   However, these numbers also duly signify the fact that to the degree of approximation of Avogadro's rule, the weights in the third column are *all* integral multiples

TABLE 3–2

Substance	STP densities, gm/liter	Weight fraction of carbon in substance, wt% C/100	Grams of carbon in 1 liter STP	Ratios of weights in preceding column	Formulas inferred from the ratios
Carbon monoxide	1.250	0.429	0.536	1	$C_1O_?$
Carbon dioxide	1.977	0.273	0.540	1	$C_1O_?$
Methane	0.717	0.750	0.538	1	$C_1H_?$
Ethane	1.357	0.799	1.084	2	$C_2H_?$
Cyanogen	2.38	0.462	1.10	2	$C_2H_?$
Trimethylboron	2.52	0.644	1.62	3	$C_3B_?H_?$
Propane	2.020	0.817	1.650	3	$C_3H_?$
Isobutane	2.673	0.827	2.211	4	$C_4H_?$

of a single minimum value: 0.536 gm/liter. Having examined an enormous number of stable carbon compounds without ever encountering a failure of this regularity, we feel well justified in writing the partial formulas shown in the last column of this table.

Now we can complete our determination of the atomic weight of nitrogen. Two methods come into consideration. The first is Cannizzaro's own, pivoting on the minimum value of 0.625 gm found in the nitrogen table, and the minimum value of 0.536 gm found in the carbon table. The 0.625 gm represents the weight of a number of nitrogen atoms numerically equal to, say, the number of molecules of nitric oxide present in 1 liter STP of that compound (which our partial formula shows to contain but 1 nitrogen atom per molecule). By the same line of reasoning, the 0.536 gm is the weight of a number of carbon atoms numerically equal to, say, the number of molecules of carbon monoxide present in 1 liter STP of that compound. But, according to Avogadro's rule, the number of molecules in 1 liter STP of carbon monoxide is *equal* to the number of molecules in 1 liter STP of nitric oxide. Hence 0.536 gm of carbon and 0.625 gm of nitrogen contain *equal* numbers of atoms of carbon and nitrogen, respectively. It then follows that the ratio of the atomic masses is $n/c = 0.625/0.536$. And now we can at once substitute in our equation defining relative atomic weights, to find the atomic weight of nitrogen (symbolized N) relative to $C \equiv 12.0$:

$$\frac{N}{C} = \frac{n}{c}, \qquad N = 12.0 \cdot \frac{0.625}{0.536} = 14.0.$$

This very satisfactory conclusion goes well beyond any previously obtained, for we could not before relate the gaseous elements to our non-gaseous standard of relative atomic weights: carbon. Note too that we have found no need to invoke the figure 22.4, obtained by other methods. The present method is then self-sufficient. On the other hand, it is only *approximate*. To get our result, we had to apply Avogadro's rule to assert the equality of the number of molecules in 1 liter STP of nitric oxide and 1 liter STP of carbon monoxide. Since Avogadro's rule does not apply rigorously to real gases at finite pressures, this may not be an exact equality, and no exact determination of atomic weight can be founded on it. This shortcoming is, however, completely removed in the second mode of proceeding, which follows.

Putting together the results indicated in the last column of each of our two tables, we see that we have completely established the formula of the carbon-nitrogen compound *cyanogen*. No uncertainty attaches to that formula. To obtain it, we need use Avogadro's rule *only* as an approximation—because, in establishing the formula, we have the support of a boundary restriction demanding that such a formula involve only small whole numbers. And with such a formula in hand, we can now go the rest of the way without any further invocation of Avogadro's rule. We need only exploit accessible combining-weight data, as described in Chapter 1. Cyanogen contains 53.835% by weight of nitrogen and, correspondingly, 46.165% by weight of carbon. On the basis of the formula C_2N_2, we can write for this compound:

$$\text{gram-atoms nitrogen} = \text{gram-atoms carbon,}$$

$$\frac{\text{grams nitrogen}}{\text{atomic weight nitrogen}} = \frac{\text{grams carbon}}{\text{atomic weight carbon}}.$$

With $C \equiv 12.011$ as our accurate reference standard, we substitute to find

$$\frac{53.835}{\text{atomic weight nitrogen}} = \frac{46.165}{12.011} ; \qquad \text{atomic weight nitrogen} = 14.007.$$

This completes a mode of operation obviously generalizable to every other element that forms a sufficient number of gaseous or volatile compounds to permit us to prepare tables like those shown above. From *each* such table—using Avogadro's rule only as an approximation, and calling for support only on an odd-number assumption that becomes stronger the more extensive the table—we can deduce the partial formulas of compounds, as well as the complete formula of the molecule of the element if it is itself volatile.* By putting together results drawn from two or more such tables, we can obtain the complete formulas for a variety of compounds, as seen in the case of cyanogen discussed above.† With these formulas in hand, we then proceed by way of combining-weight data to atomic weights, whose accuracy is limited only by the (high) accuracy with which combining weights can be established.

Our quest for a method of making accurate assignments of atomic weights has here achieved a very satisfactory consummation. But what we have found is still a method of limited applicability. Only about one-third of the known elements form a sufficient variety of volatile compounds to be treated by this method. We have still to find a method (or methods) competent to deal with the remaining two-thirds, and to this matter we now turn.

---

* We find that while many elements form diatomic molecules (for example, H_2, N_2, O_2, etc.), others have quite different degrees of complexity (for example, Hg_1, P_4, S_8, etc.).

† This procedure will allow us to establish, for example, that the formula of carbon dioxide is CO_2, as assumed—*then* without justification—in problems at the end of Chapters 1 and 2.

The Dulong-and-Petit Method

The empirical regularity on which our next development turns involves the "specific heats" of the elements. We begin with a brief examination of what the concept "specific heat" signifies and how numerical values for specific heats can be established experimentally.

Specific heats. As the unit of heat we use the *calorie*. Today the calorie is a derived quantity defined, in effect, as the quantity of heat liberated when a 1-amp current flows through a 1-ohm resistance for 4.18 sec. This definition, however, is framed to conform very closely with the historical (and more immediately meaningful) definition of the calorie as the "specific heat" of water—that is, the quantity of heat required to warm 1 gm of water by 1°C (or 1°K). For our purposes it will be sufficiently accurate to consider that this definition applies to all 1° intervals within the liquid range of water: actually the specific heat of liquid water varies slightly with temperature (which is one of the reasons that the calorie is defined today in other terms).

We next observe that in the absence of any conversion of heat to or from work, or any other form of energy, heat is apparently *conserved*. Suppose, for example, that we mix 500 gm of water at 100°C with 500 gm of water at 0°C in a well insulated container of negligible mass.* We find that (to the accuracy with which the specific heat of water *is* a constant between 0° and 100°C) the final temperature is then 50°C. Thus, the heat gained by the cold water [$= 500(50 - 0)(1) = 2500$ cal] is equal to the heat lost by the hot water [$= 500(50 - 100)(1) = -2500$ cal]. Observe that by convention, in such calculations we always subtract the *initial* temperature of the body from its *final* temperature. For the body that gains heat, the heat term will then be *positive*, since for this body the final temperature will be *greater* than the initial temperature. And, similarly, for the body that *loses* heat, the heat term will be *negative*, since for this body the final temperature will be *less* than the initial temperature. If we take care to conform to this convention, *the sum of all the heat terms will be zero*.

That the appearance of a conservation of heat in the above example is not fortuitous can be established by making other similar trials. If we mix 200 gm of water at 0°C with 800 gm of water at 100°C, the resulting mixture stands at 80°C; and again the heat gained by the cold water [$= 200(80 - 0)(1) = 1600$ cal] is numerically equal to the heat

---

* This restriction is made to ensure that no appreciable quantity of heat will be gained from or lost to the container. We shall soon find a way to lift this unrealistic stipulation.

lost by the hot water [= 800(80 − 100)(1) = −1600 cal]. Of course there is nothing special about the temperatures 0° and 100°C. If we mix a weight of *water* at 20°C with an equal weight of *water* at 40°C, the resulting mixture stands at 30°C. Moreover, if such experiments are conducted with materials other than water, the same kind of results obtain. For example, if one substitutes the word *mercury* for *both* appearances of the word *water* in the last example, nothing else need be altered. On the other hand, if our mixing operation involves *different* hot and cold bodies, we no longer find the same results. If, say, we drop a 500-gm slug of metallic nickel, warmed to 64°C, into 500 gm of water at 20°C, the final temperature is not 42°C [= (20 + 64)/2] but rather 24°C.

We are loathe to abandon a conservation law that works so well when hot and cold bodies consist of the same substance. We shall not abandon it. For it is easy to see that, so far, we have failed to make allowance for a vital consideration that becomes effective only when hot and cold bodies consist of different substances. Though it takes 1 cal to warm 1 gm of water 1°C, we have absolutely no basis for assuming that 1 cal will also be required to warm 1 gm of, say, nickel by 1°C. We must instead assign to each substance a *specific heat* defined as follows:

The specific heat of a substance is the number of calories required to warm 1 gm of that substance 1°C.

In view of our definition of the calorie, the specific heat of water is 1. And if then we encounter a substance said to have a specific heat of 0.33, this means simply that it takes just $\frac{1}{3}$ as much heat to warm 1 gm of that substance by 1°C as it takes to warm 1 gm of water by 1°C.

How are such specific heats to be determined? Most easily, by just the kind of experiment we have been discussing. Consider the trial in which nickel at one temperature was dropped into water at another. To warm 500 gm of water from 20° to 24°C we require

$$500(24 - 20)(1) \text{ cal},$$

where the (1) stands for the specific heat of water. Note that this heat term, obtained by subtracting the initial temperature from the final temperature, is appropriately positive. Where did these 200 cal come from? Consider that in cooling from 64° to 24°C, the nickel will have yielded a quantity of heat given by the expression

$$500(24 - 64)\sigma_{Ni} \text{ cal},$$

where σ_{Ni} stands for the specific heat of nickel. Note that this heat term is appropriately negative. Now, on our conservation principle, the (positive) heat gained by the water and the (negative) heat lost by the nickel must sum to zero. Hence we write

$$500(24 - 20)(1) + 500(24 - 64)\sigma_{Ni} = 0,$$
$$4 + (-40)\sigma_{Ni} = 0,$$
$$\sigma_{Ni} = 0.1 \text{ cal/gm-}°C.$$

By maintaining the conservation law, which at first seemed to be flouted, we have established a particular numerical value for the specific heat of nickel.

What about the unrealistic stipulation excluding loss or gain of heat by the container? This restriction is easily removed. We propose now to work with a "calorimeter" that can be represented by any well-insulated vessel. For our work with the Dulong-and-Petit law we need only crude results, and a calorimeter as simple as that sketched in Fig. 3–4 will serve well enough. To 50 gm of water at 20°C—contained within, and in thermal equilibrium with, a calorimeter vessel—we can, in a real experiment, add 50 gm of water at 24°C. We then find that, instead of the expected 22°C, the final temperature comes to only 21.8°C. Over this short span of temperatures the specific heat of water is effectively constant. Why then did we not find a final temperature of 22°C? For an obvious reason: beyond warming water initially at 20°C, heat was further expended in warming the interior of a calorimeter also initially at 20°C. Let w_{cal} represent the (indeterminate) weight of calorimeter in thermal contact with the water, and let σ_{cal} represent the (perhaps unknown) specific heat of the calorimeter material. For the heat acquired by the calorimeter we have then

$$w_{cal}(21.8 - 20)\sigma_{cal};$$

for the heat acquired by the cold water,

$$50(21.8 - 20)(1);$$

and for the (negative) heat given up by the warm water,

$$50(21.8 - 24)(1).$$

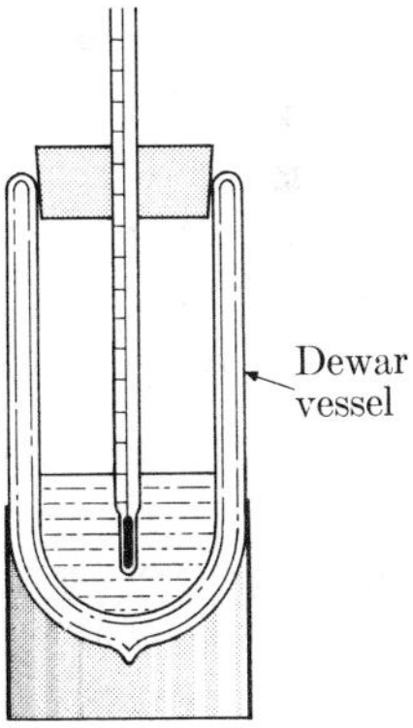

Dewar vessel

Figure 3–4

By our conservation law, all these heat terms must sum to zero:

$$w_{cal}(21.8 - 20)\sigma_{cal} + 50(21.8 - 20)(1) + 50(21.8 - 24) = 0.$$

This is an equation in two unknowns, but observe that we have no need for w_{cal} and σ_{cal} *individually*. All we need is their product, which we symbolize as C and call the "heat capacity" of the calorimeter (i.e. the total number of calories required to warm it 1°). We can then easily solve for C:

$$1.8\ C + 50(1.8) + 50(-2.2) = 0;$$

$$C = \frac{50(0.4)}{1.8} = 11\ \text{cal}/1°.$$

Once the magnitude of this heat capacity is thus established, we can go on to use the calorimeter for the determination of unknown specific heats. We charge it with 100 gm of water (to preserve roughly the same wetted surface as when the heat capacity was measured) and let the system equilibrate at, say, 20.0°. Proceeding then with alacrity, we add to the water in the calorimeter a 20-gm lump of nickel that has been heated to 100°. We observe that the temperature then rises to a peak value of 21.50°. We write

$$(21.5 - 20)(11) + 100(21.5 - 20)(1) + 20(21.5 - 100)\sigma_{Ni} = 0,$$

$$111(1.5) + 20(-78.5)\sigma_{Ni} = 0,$$

$$\sigma_{Ni} = 0.107\ \text{cal/gm-°C}.$$

As we proceed now to consider an empirical regularity found in specific heats, we can do so with full assurance that we do have empirical methods for establishing the magnitudes of these parameters.

Dulong and Petit's law. Cannizzaro's method, applicable to any element that forms a considerable variety of volatile compounds, permits us to establish the atomic weights of all the nonmetallic elements and some of the metals. Aside from the noble gases (discussed in the last section of this chapter), the considerable number of elements to which we have yet to assign atomic weights are all *solid metallic elements.* How shall we proceed with them? A plausible way to begin would be to search for some regularity involving those metals to which atomic weights are already assignable. We might then be able to extrapolate this regularity to the calculation of the atomic weights of all the remaining metals.

In Table 3–3 are listed some of the metallic elements that form enough volatile compounds to permit us to assign atomic weights by the method of Cannizzaro. As indicated in the first column of figures, the measured specific heats of these elements spread over a considerable range. In 1819 Dulong and Petit sought to explain this variation by way of the following argument. Recall that specific heats refer to *one-gram* amounts of material. The specific heats of the elements thus refer to entirely *different numbers of atoms* of these elements. For consider the very substantial spread of the atomic weights shown in the second column of the table. Looking only at the extremes, we see that one gram of aluminum represents $\frac{1}{27}$ of one gram-atom of this metal, while one gram of lead represents only

TABLE 3–3

Element	Specific heat, cal/gm-°C at 25°C	Atomic weight	Molar heat capacity, cal/mole-°C
Aluminum	0.215	27.0	5.8
Titanium	0.125	47.9	6.0
Iron	0.107	55.85	6.0
Gallium	0.090	69.7	6.3
Germanium	0.085	72.6	6.2
Tin	0.053	118.7	6.3
Antimony	0.050	121.8	6.1
Lead	0.031	207.2	6.4

$\frac{1}{207}$ of one gram-atom of this element. Hence one gram of aluminum will contain about 7.7 ($= \frac{207}{27}$) times as many atoms of aluminum as there are atoms of lead in one gram of lead. One is then led to ask (as Dulong and Petit in fact did ask) whether some more intelligible order might be found by reducing specific heats, measured for equal weights, to a common basis of *equal numbers of atoms*.

How shall we perform this reduction? If we multiply the specific heat of each metal by its atomic weight, the product will represent the number of calories required to raise by 1° the temperature of one gram-atom, or mole, of this metal. That is

$$\text{specific heat} \left(\frac{\text{calories}}{\text{gram-°C}}\right) \times \text{gram-atomic weight} \left(\frac{\text{grams}}{\text{mole}}\right)$$
$$= \text{molar heat capacity} \left(\frac{\text{calories}}{\text{mole-°C}}\right).$$

The product refers to the common basis of 1 mole of each element, and thus represents a quantity of heat reduced in every case to the common basis of an equal number of atoms. When the indicated products are computed from the figures entered in the first and second columns, we obtain the results shown in the third column—the so-called molar heat capacities.

Looking at these figures, we see that they all stand in the vicinity of 6.0. To be sure, they are not exactly the same. But note that while the specific heats spread over a wide range (the highest is seven times the lowest), the molar heat capacities lie close together (the highest is just 1.1 times the lowest). Thus it appears that the *heat capacity per gram-atom* is, to a first approximation, a constant for these elements. We can then provisionally state the law of Dulong and Petit, as follows:

$$\text{specific heat} \times \text{atomic weight} \doteq 6.0.$$

TABLE 3–4

Element	Specific heat at 25°C, in cal/gm-°C	Atomic weight	Molar heat capacity, cal/mole-°C
Boron	0.27	10.8	2.9
Carbon	0.17	12.0	2.1
Silicon	0.17	28.1	4.8
Phosphorus	0.18	31.0	5.5
Sulfur	0.17	32.1	5.4
Arsenic	0.080	74.9	6.0
Selenium	0.076	79.0	6.0
Iodine	0.052	126.9	6.6

If this is indeed a general regularity, it should apply not only to metallic solids but to other solid elements as well.* Many of the nonmetallic elements, with atomic weights readily assignable by Cannizzaro's method, exist at room temperature as solids. Will the relation tentatively established for metals apply also to nonmetals? A glance at the last column of the above table (3–4) is not very encouraging. To be sure, the molar heat capacities for the three heaviest elements fall well within the range indicated in the previous table, and even the three next heaviest elements fall not far beyond that range. But the entries for the two lightest elements fall very far out of line. What are we then to say of the alleged regularity? It would be unduly hasty to discard our provisional generalization, simply because the approximation to constancy is not as close as we could wish, and breaks down very badly for the two lightest of the 16 species of atoms we have considered. The generalization may well be perfectly genuine but subject to perturbation by secondary effects (as Boyle's-law behavior is perturbed by the nonideality of real gases). What secondary effects ought we to consider? We noted in the case of water that the specific heat (and hence the molar heat capacity) is slightly variable with temperature. And in general the specific heats (and molar heat capacities) of *all* substances in a given state manifest a gradual increase with temperature. We are then well advised to consider the possible involvement of this effect in the apparent failures of our provisional regularity.

The data presented graphically in Fig. 3–5 throw a brilliant light on the entire situation. Our difficulty can now be put in focus. All solid elements *do* seem to make a close approach to the same limiting molar heat capacity at high temperatures. But the specific heats (and the molar heat capacities) listed in our two tables are simply data collected at the most *con-*

---

* It fairly obviously fails to apply to gaseous elements; see p. 98.

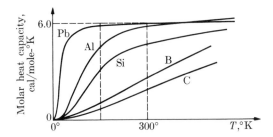

Figure 3–5

venient working temperature—"room temperature," ca. 300°K. At room temperature the heat capacities of the lightest elements are still far from their limiting values. Consider too that what happens to be "room temperature" for us is surely not a matter of fundamental significance. Were 150°K our "room temperature," Dulong-and-Petit-law behavior would be rare indeed; if "room temperature" were 1000°K, the regularity in our tabulated data would have been overwhelmingly obvious. Clearly these are only matters of "accident," and we can now readily see our way to a considerable refinement of Dulong and Petit's law.

We write this law as before: specific heat × atomic weight ≐ 6.0. For each element to be considered, however, we now stipulate that a study be made of the variation of its specific heat with temperature. At temperatures approaching 0°K the specific heats of all substances are very small. With rise of temperature, the specific heats increase more or less swiftly to a plateau value.* *It is the plateau value of the specific heat that must be inserted in the Dulong-and-Petit equation.* Acting on this policy, we find the Dulong-and-Petit law free from conspicuous exceptions—though still only approximate. Actually, knowing now what caused our original difficulty, we need not always carry through the entire study stipulated above. That is, for the heavier elements we can, without qualms, continue to use specific heats measured at room temperature: these will surely be plateau values, since the specific heats of the heavier elements rise quite rapidly to their limiting values. It is only with the lighter elements that, in order to eliminate the secondary complication, we must carry through a full range of specific-heat studies permitting us to establish the plateau values.

By stipulating the use of plateau specific heats, we eliminate from our tables all molar heat capacities appreciably lower than 6.0. Our graph shows, for example, that even at room temperature the metallic element

---

* Actually the plateau is slightly tilted: at higher temperatures, the specific heats drift very gradually toward higher values. But the stage at which the specific heat *first* acquires a plateau value is unmistakable.

aluminum has not quite reached its specific-heat plateau. When we use the actual plateau value for aluminum, its calculated molar heat capacity will move up—to a value somewhat above 6.0. With the elimination of all the low values of molar heat capacity, the center of the range of variation of this parameter rises to approximately 6.3. Still one more possible refinement makes allowance for a tertiary complication. When a substance is heated at constant pressure, part of the heat invested may be dissipated, e.g. as work done against the pressure of the atmosphere, which opposes the expansion of the substance. Just as Avogadro's hypothesis applies accurately only when we carry out an extrapolation to zero pressure, Dulong and Petit's law applies best when the molar heat capacities of the elements are corrected to eliminate such (variable) tertiary effects. The details of this calculation need not concern us: the corrections are in general quite small. If we waive consideration of the tertiary complications, the uncorrected form of Dulong and Petit's law will read:

$$\text{specific heat} \times \text{atomic weight} \doteq 6.3.$$

If, on the other hand, we propose to use only specific heats carefully corrected for the tertiary effects, Dulong and Petit's law would then be written:

$$\text{corrected specific heat} \times \text{atomic weight} \doteq 6.0.$$

What is the pedigree of Dulong and Petit's law and, more particularly, what is the theoretical significance of the corrected constant 6.0? Almost a century ago Boltzmann pointed out that, if one makes certain simplifying assumptions, the law is readily derivable from classical statistical mechanics. This derivation makes it clear that the empirical constant represents the magnitude $3R$, where R is the ideal-gas-law constant, which (as we saw on p. 65) has the magnitude 2.0 cal/mole-°K. We cannot enter here into an exposition of this derivation. Nor can we discuss the quantum theory of statistical mechanics first proposed by Einstein (and later refined by Debye and others), from which Dulong and Petit's law is even more convincingly derivable—if only because it now for the first time becomes possible to explain why the molar heat capacities of all elements are very low at temperatures approaching 0°K, and why the molar heat capacities of the lighter elements reach their plateau values only at comparatively high temperatures. Actually these theoretical justifications of Dulong and Petit's law fall far beyond the realm of our present inquiry—even though, in the apparently analogous case presented by Avogadro's hypothesis, we took theoretical justification to be a matter of crucial importance. How do the two cases differ?

Avogadro's hypothesis is but one of many possible *theoretical* statements concordant with the experimental facts (see p. 25), and we dared not rely on it until it had been justified as Avogadro's rule. Dulong and Petit's law, on the other hand, is a largely *empirical* statement—just as is, for example, the law of equivalent proportions. Though the theoretical justification of Dulong and Petit's law is most welcome, the law exists as an empirical generalization quite independent of that justification. We can then at once press forward with Dulong and Petit's law, treating it as a purely empirical regularity that promises some support to our efforts to assign atomic weights to the elements. But *can* that law help us assign accurate atomic weights when, particularly in the uncorrected form we shall use, the law is approximate to the extent of at least 5%? The answer to this query is already foreshadowed by the way in which we used Avogadro's rule. That rule is also only an approximation, as applied to real gases. But, supported by the boundary condition that the formulas of compounds must involve only small whole numbers, Avogadro's rule does permit us to establish these formulas. And though, particularly in its uncorrected form, Dulong and Petit's law is not at all as good an approximation as Avogadro's rule, we can use the former exactly as we did the latter. An illustrative example will make the situation clear.

Illustrative Example. An oxide of the element tantalum (symbol, Ta) contains 81.90% by weight of that metallic element. Given that the measured specific heat of tantalum is 0.036 cal/gm-°K and that the atomic weight of oxygen is 16.00, calculate the accurate atomic weight of tantalum.

Let the formula of the tantalum oxide be represented as Ta_xO_y. We can then write

$$\frac{y}{x} \cdot \text{gram-atoms Ta} = \text{gram-atoms O},$$

$$\frac{y}{x} \cdot \frac{81.90}{\text{atomic weight Ta}} = \frac{18.10}{16.00},$$

$$\text{atomic weight Ta} = \frac{y}{x} \, 72.40.$$

Turning now to Dulong and Petit's law, we obtain an approximate value for the atomic weight of tantalum:

$$\text{specific heat Ta} \times \text{atomic weight Ta} \doteq 6.3,$$

$$\text{atomic weight Ta} \doteq \frac{6.3}{0.036} = 175.$$

Were we now to assign $y/x = 2$, we would find 144.8 as the atomic weight of tantalum; were we to assign $y/x = 3$, we would find 217.2 for the atomic weight of tantalum. Both these figures fall well *outside* the range of uncertainty left by the approximateness of Dulong and Petit's law. However, if we assign $y/x = \frac{5}{2}$, we obtain the result 181.0. That is

$$\text{atomic weight Ta} = \tfrac{5}{2} \times 72.40 = 181.0,$$

and this agrees with the Dulong-and-Petit estimate to well *within* the range of uncertainty attached to that estimate. Thus we assign the formula Ta_2O_5 to the tantalum oxide, and 181.0 as the atomic weight of tantalum.

Observe that where Avogadro's rule yielded the molecular formulas of gaseous compounds, Dulong and Petit's law yields only the *empirical* formulas of solid compounds; e.g. in the illustrative example we obtained only the *ratio $y/x = \frac{5}{2}$* and *not* the values of y and x *individually*. In principle we might well *prefer* to have molecular formulas; but we will find in Chapter 5 that, when we speak of many solid compounds, it is very doubtful that anything more than an empirical formula is meaningful. And in any case, insofar as the calculation of atomic weights is concerned, it is clear that all we actually need is an *empirical* formula, and this we *are* able to assign with the aid of Dulong and Petit's law. Thus Dulong and Petit's law does at last permit us to assign accurate atomic weights to all the metallic elements that (because they form no great variety of volatile compounds) could not before be assigned atomic weights by the method of Cannizzaro.* We have then very nearly completed our task: the systematic assignment of accurate atomic weights to *all* the elements. The only elements with which we are still unable to deal are the so-called noble gases— He, Ne, Ar, Kr, and Xe—and to these elements we now turn.

The Noble Gases

The recent discovery that xenon forms a number of reasonably stable volatile compounds does not at all improve the present prospect of finding comparable compounds formed by the lighter members of the group of noble gases. We must then discover some way of assigning accurate atomic weights to these elements for which we do not have (and presumably never will have) the accurate combining-weight data that have heretofore been our ultimate reliance. How shall we proceed? All these elements are gases— and comparatively ideal gases at that—and it is then reasonable to look to the method of limiting gas densities as a way of establishing *accurate* molecular weights even in the absence of combining-weight data. But these *molecular* weights will be translatable into accurate *atomic* weights only if we can find some method for assigning *molecular formulas* to the

---

* Observe that once Dulong and Petit's law points to an approximate atomic weight for the element in question, the availability of even *one* volatile compound of that element will permit us to deploy Avogadro's rule to assign a formula to that compound. [*Query:* How?] Thus, tantalum forms a volatile compound to which we can assign the molecular formula $TaCl_5$, and from the measured combining weights for this compound we obtain a value confirming the atomic weight we have assigned to tantalum.

gaseous particles of these elements. Concerned as we are with gases that fail to form compounds, neither combining-volume data nor a Cannizzaro-style analysis can be expected to help us. Will heat-capacity data be of assistance? How can we obtain such data?

The comparative minuteness of gaseous heat capacities makes them very difficult to measure directly. Ordinarily the heat capacity of a gas is dwarfed by the heat capacity of the container in which it is held, and accurate results are not then readily obtainable. We may hope to deal with this difficulty by arranging to heat the gas very rapidly and to measure its peak temperature before any substantial amount of heat can be transferred to the walls of the container. An effort to realize this possibility is reflected in Fig. 3–6. A flask of known volume (V) is loaded with the gas in question at ambient temperature (T) and pressure (P)—that is, loaded with a calculable number of moles, $n = PV/RT$. The large capacitor is charged by connecting it with a battery. We then throw the switch to discharge the capacitor through the resistance wire inside the flask. This essentially instantaneous transfer of electrical energy to the gas produces a sharp rise of its temperature. The system being one of effectively constant volume, the magnitude of the temperature rise can be established, with the aid of Amontons' law, from the maximum reading of the (fast-acting) manometer.* Denoting by T' and P' the temperature and pressure of the gas immediately after the discharge of the condenser, we write

$$\frac{P'}{P} = \frac{T'}{T},$$

so that

$$\frac{P'}{P} - 1 = \frac{T'}{T} - 1$$

and

$$\frac{P' - P}{P} = \frac{T' - T}{T},$$

in which case

$$\frac{\Delta P}{P} = \frac{\Delta T}{T},$$

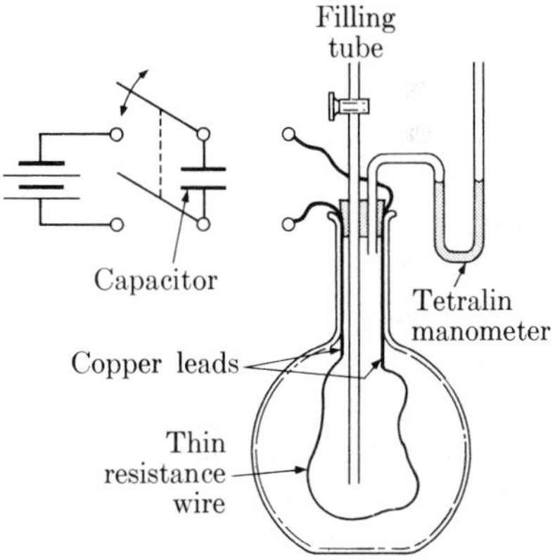

Figure 3–6

---

* When the reading of peak pressure is made, some of the gas (close to the wire) may stand at a temperature appreciably higher than the temperature of the bulk of the gas in the flask. From Problem 9 on p. 103 it can readily be seen that this nonuniformity of the gas temperature has no effect whatever on the above calculation.

TABLE 3–5

Gaseous element	Molar heat capacity C_V, cal/mole-°K	Gaseous element	Molar heat capacity C_V, cal/mole-°K
P_4*	14	He?	3.0
Cl_2	6.1	Ne?	3.0
O_2	5.0	Ar?	3.0
N_2	5.0	Kr?	3.0
H_2	4.9	Xe?	3.0
Hg_1*	3.0		

* From high-temperature work.

where ΔP and ΔT represent the increases in pressure and temperature consequent to discharge of the condenser. The magnitude ΔP is precisely what is indicated by the maximum displacement reached by the liquid levels in the manometer; and the original pressure (P) and temperature (T) of the gas are, of course, known to us. From the equation

$$\Delta T = (T/P)\,\Delta P$$

we can then establish the magnitude of the temperature rise (ΔT) produced by the delivery of a known quantity of energy (J) to a known number of moles of gas (n). The constant-volume heat capacity of the gas (C_V) is now accessible by way of the relation

$$n \text{ (moles)} \times C_V \left(\frac{\text{cal}}{\text{mole-°K}}\right) \times \Delta T \text{ (°K)} = J \text{ (cal)}$$

or

$$C_V = J/n\,\Delta T.$$

We thus obtain results like those shown in Table 3–5.*

An extension to gases of the Dulong-and-Petit law, worked out for solids, looks distinctly unpromising. Recall, moreover, that this law refers to gram-*atomic* weights of the elements. In the case of gaseous phosphorus the indicated gram-atomic heat capacity is only 3.5 $(= \frac{1}{4} \times 14.0)$; for

---

* Though simple in principle, the experimental technique here described yields only approximate results: see D. L. Livesey, *Am. J. Phys.* **33**, 18 (1965). Ordinarily we prefer to rely on other methods that, though less direct, are capable of higher accuracy. A great variety of methods, e.g., determination of the velocity of sound in the gas under consideration, furnish excellent values for a certain parameter γ. From this parameter, C_V is readily calculated by way of the theoretically derivable equation $C_V = R/(\gamma - 1)$, where R is again the ideal-gas-law constant.

oxygen it is only 2.5, and so on. These figures are *far* less than the Dulong-and-Petit figure 6. Nor can we hope to improve the situation by seeking plateau values for the gaseous heat capacities: many of the data entered in our table are in fact values corresponding to a very long plateau already attained well below room temperature. Thus there is *no* prospect that we can bring Dulong and Petit's law to bear on these gaseous elements. Happily, however, we can easily snatch victory from the jaws of this apparently conclusive defeat—by pursuing a line of theoretical analysis for which the foundation has already been laid.

On p. 66 we found that the translational kinetic energy of a mole of ideal gas can be expressed as $\frac{3}{2}RT$. If the gas is monatomic, we see no way in which it can store thermal energy save as translational kinetic energy, and in this case $\frac{3}{2}RT$ will represent the *total* thermal energy of the gas. At $T°$K the gas has thermal energy $\frac{3}{2}RT$; at $(T + 1)°$K it has thermal energy $\frac{3}{2}R(T + 1)$. Hence, to warm one mole of ideal monatomic gas by 1°K, we will have to supply it with energy $= \frac{3}{2}R(T + 1) - \frac{3}{2}RT = \frac{3}{2}R$. That is, $\frac{3}{2}R$ must represent the molar heat capacity of the gas, *provided that* heat capacity is measured under constant-volume conditions which obviate the dissipative effects noted on p. 94. Knowing that $R = 2.0$ cal/mole-°K, we thus deduce that an ideal monatomic gas will have $C_V = 3.0$ cal/mole-°K.* Turning then to polyatomic gases, we see that even though $\frac{3}{2}RT$ will still represent the translational kinetic energy, *they* can store thermal energy in other ways: e.g. in rotational and vibrational motions of the polyatomic molecule. The translational energy is then but one contributor to a total energy we represent as qRT, where q stands for some number greater than $\frac{3}{2}$. For a polyatomic gas, therefore, we have $C_V = qRT > \frac{3}{2}R$, which is to say $C_V > 3.0$ cal/mole-°K. A glance at the tabulated values for C_V shows that the more complex molecular species *do* have higher values for C_V. And, much more important, we observe

---

* How does this figure relate to the heat capacity of one gram-atom of a solid element, with atoms vibrating around their equilibrium positions in the crystal? Assuming that the restoring force acting on any vibrating atom is always proportional to the displacement of that atom from its equilibrium position in the crystal, Ludwig Boltzmann was able to construct a theoretical demonstration that, at any given temperature, the energy associated with a vibrational motion in one dimension is twice the energy associated with a free translational motion in one dimension. We have found that one mole of ideal monatomic gas particles, in free translational motion in three dimensions, possesses a thermal energy $\frac{3}{2}RT$ and a heat capacity of 3.0 cal/mole-°K. Hence, one mole of atoms vibrating in three dimensions, within a crystalline solid, will possess a thermal energy $\frac{6}{2}RT$ and a heat capacity of 6.0 cal/mole-°K. This is, in brief, the origin of the figure 6.0 in the corrected form of Dulong and Petit's law. For a somewhat fuller account of the argument, see R. K. Fitzgerel and F. Verhoek, *J. Chem. Educ.* **37,** 545 (1960).

METHODS OF ASSIGNING ATOMIC WEIGHTS TO ELEMENTS

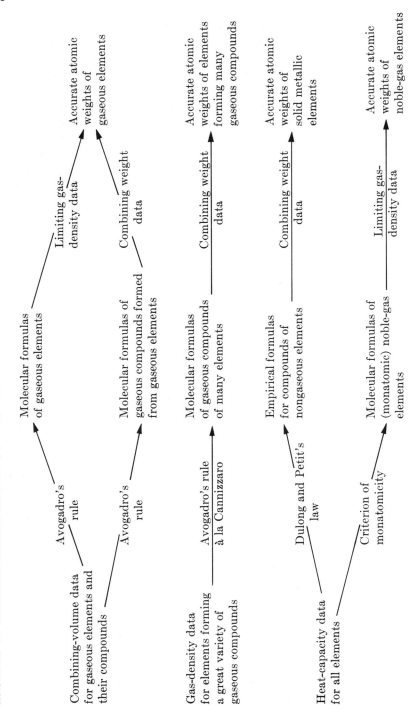

that mercury, whose gaseous particle is shown by Cannizzaro's method to be monatomic, does have $C_V = 3.0$ cal/mole-°K. We have here a superlative empirical confirmation of our theoretical analysis. And we need then have no hesitation in concluding that the empirical result $C_V = 3.0$ cal/mole-°K, applying to all the noble gases, is an unequivocal indication that all the noble gases are monatomic. Thus it follows that the accurate relative molecular weights of these elements, determined by the method of limiting densities, represent also the accurate atomic weights. And with this finding we bring to completion our systematic assignment of accurate atomic weights to the chemical elements. A diagrammatic summary of all the methods developed in the last two chapters is provided on the facing page.

PROBLEMS

1. In a determination conducted at 450°C and a pressure of 723 mm Hg, a Dumas bulb was found to contain 1.60 gm of sulfur (atomic weight, 32). When the bulb was opened under water, a weight gain of 390 gm was observed, apparently signifying 390 ml as the volume of the bulb.
   (a) What is (i) the molecular weight and (ii) the molecular formula of sulfur vapor under these conditions?
   (b) Actually the volume of the bulb is 400 ml, and the figure 390 ml was found only because (due to defective performance of the experiment) 10 ml of air still remained in the bulb when it was sealed off. This air is, indeed, plainly visible as a 10-ml bubble in the flask after it has been "filled" with water. What, if any, error is thus introduced into the calculated molecular weight of sulfur?

2. When solid UCl_4 is heated in the presence of H_2, some HCl gas is formed together with a solid residue that still contains only uranium and chlorine. In a 500-ml vessel are placed 0.760 gm of UCl_4 and H_2 at a pressure of 1.00 atm and a temperature of 27°C. The system is then heated to 300°C and, at the conclusion of the chemical reaction, the final pressure is observed to be 2.005 atm. Assuming that both the uranium chlorides involved are substantially involatile at 300°C, calculate:
   (a) The H_2 pressure that would have existed at 300°C had no reaction occurred.
   (b) The pressure of hydrogen chloride actually present at 300°C.
   (c) The moles of hydrogen chloride evolved.
   (d) The moles of UCl_4 originally present.
   (e) The formula of the resultant chloride.
   (Atomic weights: U, 238; Cl, 35.5.)

3. A certain compound of hydrogen and carbon contains 14.3% hydrogen. Incomplete combustion of 50 ml of the hydrocarbon vapor, measured at

273°C and 760 mm Hg, yielded 0.3708 gm of CO_2, 0.1427 gm of H_2O, and an undetermined quantity of methane, CH_4. Compute:

(a) the empirical formula of the compound,

(b) the grams of methane formed,

(c) the molecular formula of the compound.

(Atomic weights: H, 1; C, 12; O, 16.)

4. A sample of hafnium metal weighing 5.00 gm requires 0.170 calories to warm it 1°C. When this sample reacts with oxygen, 5.896 gm of hafnium oxide is produced.

   (a) Compute the approximate atomic weight of hafnium, taking 6.3 as the Dulong-and-Petit constant.

   (b) Determine the empirical formula of the hafnium oxide.

   (c) Calculate the accurate atomic weight of hafnium relative to oxygen taken as 16.

5. The metal M has a specific heat of 0.15 cal/gm-°C. When the metal bromide is heated in a stream of HCl gas, it is completely converted to the metallic chloride of analogous formula. From 1.878 gm of the bromide just 1.000 gm of the chloride is obtained. Compute:

   (a) the approximate atomic weight of the metal,

   (b) the empirical formula of the halides,

   (c) the accurate atomic weight of M.

   (Atomic weights: Cl, 35.5; Br, 79.9.)

6. Substances I, II, III, IV, and V all contain the element bromine. The data in Table 3–6 are available.

TABLE 3–6

	Density of the gaseous substance	Percent of bromine in the substance
Substance I	5.87	90.9
Substance II	2.70	98.8
Substance III	14.63	72.9
Substance IV	5.33	100.0
Substance V	8.50	94.1

All the density measurements were made under the same conditions of temperature and pressure, and under these conditions the density of hydrogen gas (H_2) was 0.0667. Taking 1.0 as the atomic weight of hydrogen, determine:

(a) The most probable value for the atomic weight of bromine.

(b) The molecular formula of bromine vapor.

(c) If it is known that in substance III the molecule contains, aside from bromine, just one atom of the element X, what is the atomic weight of X?

7. The specific heat of uranium (U) is 0.027 cal/gm-°C. Uranium forms a compound with the element fluorine (F; atomic weight, 19). The density of this compound is 176 times that of gaseous hydrogen (H_2) at the same temperature and pressure. What is the formula of the compound?

8. Careful measurement shows that the heat capacity of a particular lump of pure metallic antimony is 0.305 cal/°K. When subjected to chlorination, this sample of antimony reacts with 5.325 gm of chlorine (atomic weight, 35.5) to form a well defined antimony chloride.

   (a) What is the formula of this antimony chloride?

   (b) Given now that the atomic weight of antimony is 121.8, what is the *accurate* specific heat of antimony implied by the above measurement of heat capacity?

9. The experimental determination of gaseous heat capacity described on p. 97 rests on the proposition that the pressure exerted by an unevenly heated ideal gas is exactly the same as that it would exert were it to come to temperature equilibrium without change of volume and without loss of heat to the walls of its container. Imagine that some n_h moles of gas at some temperature T_h are initially present with n_l moles of the same ideal gas at the lower temperature T_l in a container of unchanging volume (V). Assume that (i) between T_l and T_h the heat capacity of the gas is constant, (ii) there is no heat transfer between the gas and the walls of the container, and (iii) all parts of the gas are at all times in pressure equilibrium with each other.

   (a) What will be the final temperature of the gas, after temperature equilibrium has been reached?

   (b) Demonstrate that the pressure of the gas when temperature equilibrium has been attained is exactly the same as the pressure (P) initially exerted by the unevenly heated gas.

CHAPTER 4

THE SYSTEMATIC ASSIGNMENT OF MOLECULAR FORMULAS

For compounds that form stable gaseous molecules, the determination of molecular formulas presents no problem: Cannizzaro's method is obviously applicable. On the other hand, once atomic weights have been established, it is entirely unnecessary to prepare lengthy Cannizzaro-style tables every time we need to establish a molecular formula. Aside from determining the composition of the compound at issue, it is necessary only to make a single relatively crude determination of the vapor-density of that compound. These data are amply sufficient for an assignment of molecular formula, as will be clear from a consideration of two simple examples.

Illustrative Example. Suppose that after assigning an atomic weight of 31.0 to phosphorus, we at last find it possible to measure the density of elemental phosphorus at high temperature. Assign a molecular formula to phosphorus vapor, given that 1.35 gm of vapor occupy 500 ml at 300°C and 750 mm Hg pressure.

In principle this is a simple problem. To phosphorus vapor we assign the formula P_x, where x is some unknown small whole number. Hence the accurate molecular weight of phosphorus vapor must be $31.0(x)$ and—given the small-whole-number restriction—even a crude determination of molecular weight will permit us to assign a value to x. We have then only to derive from our data an approximate value for the molecular weight of phosphorus vapor, and this is easy to do.

Method I. In this method we take, as a working definition of molecular weight, the number of grams of phosphorus required to fill 22.4 liters STP. We proceed by calculating the STP volume of the vapor whose weight, in grams, we already know.

$$V_{\text{STP}} = 500 \cdot \frac{750}{760} \cdot \frac{273}{273 + 300} = 235 \text{ ml STP.}$$

How many moles of phosphorus vapor do we have? If we had 22.4 liters STP we would have 1 mole; having only 0.235 liter STP, we can represent the number of moles present (n) as

$$n \doteq \frac{0.235}{22.4} = 0.0105.$$

Symbolizing by M the molecular weight of the phosphorus vapor, we can express in terms of M the numbers of grams of vapor present:

$$nM = 1.35,$$

whence

$$M = \frac{1.35}{n} \doteq \frac{1.35}{0.0105} = 129.$$

This figure is only *approximately* correct. (Why?) But we also know that $M = 31.0x$, where x is a small whole number. We then have no hesitation in assigning a value of 4 to x, and the formula P_4 to phosphorus vapor. This method is very simple conceptually, but tedious arithmetically. Let us look at another (preferable) method.

Method II. In this method we use the ideal gas law (approximately applicable to real gases) to determine directly the number of moles of gas to which our 1.35-gm sample corresponds—whence we can determine the approximate molecular weight and proceed as before. With due *attention to units*, we substitute our data in the equation $PV = nRT$, and obtain

$$(75.0)(0.500) = n(6.23)(573),$$
$$n = 0.0105.$$

That is, 0.0105 mole of phosphorus vapor weighs 1.35 gm. Hence

$$0.0105M = 1.35, \qquad M = 129,$$

and our conclusion is the same as before.

Illustrative Example. A 0.575-gm sample of a compound containing 40% carbon, 6.67% hydrogen, and 53.33% oxygen occupies a vapor volume of 362 ml at a temperature of 200°C (473°K) and 754 mm Hg pressure. Given atomic weights of 1, 12, and 16 for hydrogen, carbon, and oxygen respectively, find the molecular formula of the compound.

We begin by determining the empirical formula by the methods of Chapter 1. For a 100-gm sample of the compound we can write

$$\text{gram-atoms hydrogen present} = \frac{\text{grams hydrogen present}}{\text{atomic weight hydrogen}} = \frac{6.67}{1} = 6.67,$$

$$\text{gram-atoms carbon present} = \frac{\text{grams carbon present}}{\text{atomic weight carbon}} = \frac{40}{12} = 3.33,$$

$$\text{gram-atoms oxygen present} = \frac{\text{grams oxygen present}}{\text{atomic weight oxygen}} = \frac{53.33}{16} = 3.33.$$

Hence the *empirical* formula of the compound is $(CH_2O)_x$, where x is the small whole number to which we must assign a value if we are to obtain the desired *molecular* formula. Observe that the molecular weight (M) of the compound can now be expressed as $x[12 + 2(1) + 16] = 30x = M$. Thus, if we can find even an approximate value for the molecular weight, we will be able to establish the value of x and thence the molecular formula.

Solving by Method II, we have

$$(75.4)(0.362) = n(6.23)(473), \qquad n = 0.00925 \text{ mole},$$

$$\text{approximate molecular weight} = M = \frac{0.575}{0.00925} = 62.$$

Thus it is clear that $x = 2$, and the molecular formula of the compound is established as $C_2H_4O_2$.

This simple mode of procedure is obviously applicable to all compounds stable enough in the gas phase to permit determination of their vapor densities. But many nongaseous compounds of interest to organic chemists and biochemists cannot be so treated—simply because they decompose when strongly heated in the effort to volatilize them. The molecular formulas of such compounds are often of crucial importance: how may we hope to establish these formulas? A consideration of the principle on which the above examples were solved will suggest the line we must pursue.

In essence, we proceed as follows: (i) By use of vapor-density data, we establish the approximate number of moles (n) of substance that correspond to some known weight (w) of that substance. (ii) From n and w we can make an estimate of the molecular weight (M) of the substance; that is, $M \doteq w/n$. (iii) On the basis of combining-weight data, we can assign an empirical formula to the compound. (iv) From the empirical formula and the known atomic weights of the constituent elements, we can calculate the empirical-formula weight (μ). (v) In terms of μ and the (unknown) small whole number x, which represents the number of empirical-formula-units that enter into one molecule, we can express the accurate molecular weight as $M = \mu x$. (vi) Comparing the value of M obtained in (ii) with the value of M demanded in (v), we establish the numerical value of x. (vii) Having in hand both the empirical formula and the proper value for x, we can at once assign to the compound a molecular formula (and an accurate molecular weight).

Observe that vapor-density data are required only in step (i), where they are used to determine the number of moles (n) of compound present. And it is then clear that, were we able to find other methods for determining n, those methods would permit us to establish the molecular formulas of *involatile* compounds by exactly the same line of reasoning we have followed with volatile compounds. Just such alternative methods can be

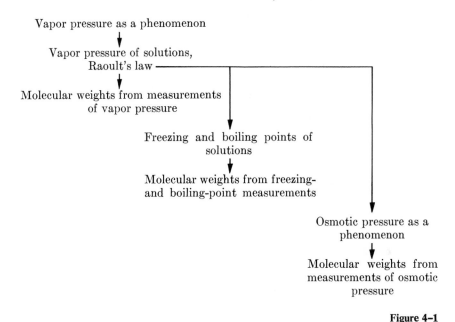

Vapor pressure as a phenomenon

Vapor pressure of solutions,
Raoult's law

Molecular weights from measurements
of vapor pressure

Freezing and boiling points of
solutions

Molecular weights from freezing-
and boiling-point measurements

Osmotic pressure as a
phenomenon

Molecular weights from
measurements of osmotic
pressure

Figure 4–1

based on a study of the "colligative properties" of solutions (i.e. the vapor-pressure lowering, boiling-point elevation, freezing-point depression, and osmotic pressure). By an appropriate choice of solvent, practically all the involatile compounds with which we are concerned *can* be dissolved. Hence there is every prospect that all our remaining difficulties can be resolved by the colligative-property methods. These methods are the subject of the remainder of the present chapter, a topical outline for which is shown in Fig. 4–1.

Expressions of Concentration

Our inquiry demands use of several different modes of expression for the empirical concentration of solutions, and we may do well to begin with a brief survey of these expressions. Two familiar ways of expressing the concentration of a solution are percent by weight and percent by volume. Observe that, whether percentages are given by weight or by volume, the percentages of all components in a given solution must add up to 100: that is, $\sum r_i = 100$, where r_i symbolizes the percentage of the ith component. Both weight and volume percentages (and particularly weight percentages) have considerable practical usefulness in chemistry. But they lack the more fundamental significance of expressions of concentration couched in terms of *moles*. Three such expressions are frequently of use. The first should already be familiar: the *molarity* of a solution expresses the number of moles of solute* *per liter of solution.* The second is equally simple: the *molality* (symbol m) of a solution expresses the number of moles of solute *per 1000 gm of pure solvent* used in making the solution. The third and most important expression is the mole fraction (symbol X). The *mole fraction* of a component in a solution is just that fraction of the *total* number of moles of all components present which corresponds to the moles of the component at issue. For a ("binary") solution containing only two components, A and B, we can then write

$$X_A = \frac{\text{moles A}}{\text{moles A + moles B}}, \qquad X_B = \frac{\text{moles B}}{\text{moles A + moles B}}.$$

Obviously $X_A + X_B = 1$ and, for the general case of a multicomponent solution, we can write the analogous expression $\sum X_i = 1$. All our work will be conducted with binary solutions. We will then symbolize the mole fraction of the solvent as X_v and the mole fraction of the solute as X_u, and for these solutions we will always be able to write $X_v + X_u = 1$. Hence, if we are able to determine *either* X_u *or* X_v, we can at once establish the other by use of the last equation.

Some *approximate* relations of molarity, molality, and mole fraction should be noted. For the special case of a *very dilute aqueous solution*, the molarity and molality will be approximately equal—since one liter of such solution will contain approximately 1000 gm of the solvent, water. However, for solvents that (unlike water) have densities very different from 1.0 gm/ml, this equality will not obtain even as an approximation. Of rather more general interest is an approximate relation linking the molality and mole fraction of solute in *very dilute solutions in any solvent.* For any such solution we can write

$$X_u = \frac{\text{moles solute}}{\text{moles solute + moles solvent}} \doteq \frac{\text{moles solute}}{\text{moles solvent}},$$

since, if the solution is dilute enough, moles solute $\ll$ moles solvent. If this condition is met, the mole *fraction* will be well approximated as the mole *ratio* indicated. Now, the solute molality (m) in a solution is simply the number of moles of solute per 1000 gm of solvent. Representing by M the molecular weight of the *solvent*, we write the mole ratio in a solution

---

* Provisionally, we may define the word "solvent" as signifying the pure liquid component preponderant in a solution, the word "solute" as signifying any other component dissolved in the solvent to form a solution. As our study progresses we will be able fully to grasp the meaning of alternative definitions that are somewhat better so far as colligative properties are concerned: the solvent is the component that distributes itself over two phases; the solute appears in but one phase.

as $m/(1000/M)$. And then, *if* the solution is dilute enough, we can also write

$$X_u \doteq \frac{mM}{1000} \qquad \text{or} \qquad m \doteq \frac{1000}{M} X_u.$$

We can estimate the applicability of these approximate relations by considering a representative solvent with $M = 200$. Suppose that we have a 0.05 molal solution of some solute in this solvent, 1000 gm of which will represent 5.0 moles. For the mole fraction of solute we write

$$X_u = \frac{0.05}{0.05 + 5.0}, \begin{cases} = 0.0099 \\ \doteq \dfrac{0.05}{5.0} = 0.01 \end{cases}$$

In this case the approximation of the mole fraction as a mole ratio introduces an error of but 1%, but for molalities >0.05 the error will become more serious.

Illustrative Example. A benzene solution of anthracene contains 10% by weight of the latter. Given that the molecular weights of benzene and anthracene are respectively 78 and 178, calculate (i) the molality of anthracene in the solution and (ii) the mole fractions of anthracene and benzene in the solution.*
    As a convenient basis for calculation, we adopt 100 gm of solution containing 10 gm of anthracene and 90 gm of benzene. The moles of anthracene present are $\frac{10}{178}$; the moles of anthracene per *one* gram of benzene are $\frac{1}{90} \cdot \frac{10}{178}$; and the moles of anthracene per *thousand* grams of benzene, i.e. the molality of anthracene, will be

$$m = \frac{1000}{90} \cdot \frac{10}{178} = 0.62.$$

Turning now to the mole fractions, we write

$$\text{mole fraction of benzene} = X_v = \frac{\text{moles benzene}}{\text{moles benzene} + \text{moles anthracene}}$$

$$= \frac{90/78}{(90/78) + (10/178)} = \frac{1.154}{1.154 + 0.056} = 0.954,$$

$$\text{mole fraction of anthracene} = X_u = 1 - X_v = 1.000 - 0.954 = 0.046.$$

Noting this mole fraction of anthracene, we may expect an error of about 5% if we attempt to approximate the mole fraction as a mole ratio. [*Query:* What is the basis for this expectation?] We confirm this prediction by using the approxi-

---

* Observe that we are not asked to calculate the *molarity* of anthracene in the solution. What one additional datum is requisite to make that calculation possible?

mate relation given above to calculate the molality of anthracene from its mole fraction:

$$m \doteq \frac{1000}{78} (0.046) = 0.59,$$

which *is* about 5% in error relative to the correct answer, 0.62.

Vapor Pressure

We preface our inquiry into the colligative properties of solutions with an extended discussion of the fundamental phenomenon of vapor pressure, as it is seen in the solvents to be used in our studies. The apparatus sketched in Fig. 4–2 offers neither the most accurate nor the most convenient method for determining vapor pressures. But it does offer one of the simplest and most obvious lines of approach to such a determination at temperatures that do not range much above 100°C. We equip an ordinary barometer tube with a jacket as shown. By passing through the jacket any suitably heated fluid, we can bring the temperature of the barometer tube (and its contents) to any desired value. Completely filling the barometer tube with mercury and inverting it in a bowl of mercury, we set up an ordinary Torricellian barometer in which the initial level of mercury in the tube is at x, about 760 mm above the mercury level in the cistern.

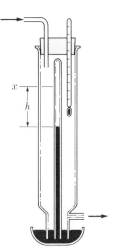

We now introduce through the bottom of the barometer a considerable quantity of the substance whose vapor pressure we wish to determine. This quantity need not be measured, but must be large enough to ensure that even at the highest vapor pressure to be measured, excess liquid (or solid) will be present.* The sample is invariably less dense than mercury and rises to float on the mercury surface in the barometer tube, where it is exposed to the temperature there prevailing. If we start at room temperature with a substantially involatile specimen,

Figure 4–2

---

* In the Hofmann determination (see p. 78) we had to introduce a *weighed* sample small enough to be *completely vaporized* at the time the vapor volume was determined. Here, on the other hand, we are interested not in vapor *density* but in vapor *pressure:* we care nothing for the weight of material vaporized, but we wish to ensure that what we measure is the *maximum* pressure the substance can develop at the given temperature. That an excess of substance *is* present we can readily ascertain by observing that there is *some* condensed sample floating atop the mercury at all stages in the experiment.

the mercury meniscus in the barometer will stand close to its original level at x. But as we raise the temperature, the mercury meniscus will be depressed farther below the level x. At each temperature the distance h offers a visible indication of the vapor pressure developed by the substance. For, after all, the depression of the mercury column occurs simply in response to the vapor pressure developed by the sample in the originally void space at the top of the barometer.* Making due correction for the (measurable) variation

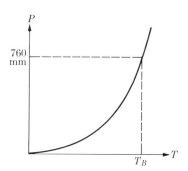

Figure 4–3

of the density of mercury with temperature, we can then infer—from the measured value of h corresponding to each working temperature—the true vapor pressure of the sample substance at that temperature. Plotting the measured vapor pressures against the corresponding temperatures, we always obtain a curve something like that shown in Fig. 4–3. Rising very slowly at low temperatures, the curve rises steeply at high temperatures. Actually, the rise is exponential throughout.

We can easily give a qualitative interpretation of the above findings—by extending to condensed phases the kinetic theory originally developed only for gases. We then imagine that, in the liquid state, the component molecules have average kinetic energies much the same as those they would have were they in the gaseous state at the same temperature. In the gas phase the molecules move essentially independently of one another and, between collisions, ordinarily traverse a distance equivalent to many particle diameters. The situation in the liquid is *very* different. Here the particles are closely packed together, and they cannot move a distance of even one particle diameter without colliding with some neighbor(s). Even more important, the intermolecular forces are here so effective that—instead of essentially independent particle motions—we have in the liquid highly constrained motions: the particles stay together rather than distributing themselves throughout the container, as they would do were they gaseous. To escape from the liquid—to pull itself free from these constraints—a particle must possess a translational kinetic energy considerably greater than the *average* kinetic energy characteristic of the temperature concerned. At each temperature the equilibrium vapor pressure is developed when the number of particles leaving the surface of the liquid is equal to the number rejoining it from the gas. Other things being equal, this

---

* The vapor pressure of mercury itself, about 0.001 mm at room temperature, is still only about 0.3 mm at 100°C.

last number may be presumed to be directly proportional to the pressure of the gas. (Consider that, on our kinetic hypothesis, "pressure" and particle collisions with any unit surface exposed to the gas are but different descriptions of the same effect.) At low temperatures, when at any one time only a very small proportion of the particles in the liquid have the requisite escape energy, the equilibrium vapor pressure developed by the liquid must be small. At high temperatures, on the other hand, when at any one time a comparatively larger proportion of the particles in the liquid have the requisite escape energy, the equilibrium vapor pressure developed by the liquid must be correspondingly larger.

The substance of the preceding paragraph is *only a hypothesis*, and a crudely stated one at that. When fully refined, this hypothesis can be subjected to a statistical mechanical development that yields predictions in quantitative agreement with the observed dependence of vapor pressure on temperature. But an entirely different (thermodynamic) mode of analysis, making no hypothesis about the physical nature of either liquids or gases, yields a much simpler derivation of the observable dependence of vapor pressure on temperature.* Excepting only one point noted in the next paragraph, these theoretical developments are of *no* immediate concern to us. For we are interested primarily in the *existence* of vapor pressure as a *phenomenon*, and not in the possibilities of supplying a *theoretical interpretation* of that phenomenon.

The only theoretical deduction of immediate interest emerges from both lines of reasoning noted above. If we represent vapor pressure by P and absolute temperature by T, it is predicted that a plot of $\log P$ vs. $1/T$ should closely approximate a straight line. Noting the form of the curve obtained on a direct P vs. T plot of our empirical data, we might have arrived at the same conclusion by trial-and-error manipulations. In any case, graphs like that in Fig. 4–4 demonstrate that $\log P$ vs. $1/T$ plots *are* approximately rectilinear. Observe that the plot now slopes up to the left. This is as it should be: with $1/T$ as abscissa, the highest temperatures will fall on the left, where the value of $1/T$ is least. Observe too that the availability of such an approximately rectilinear plot is a great practical convenience. For we can then easily interpo-

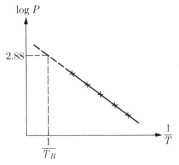

Figure 4–4

---

* This dependence is expressed in the so-called Clausius-Clapeyron equation. For a simple derivation of this equation see pp. 64–66 in Nash, *Elements of Chemical Thermodynamics*, Addison-Wesley Pub. Co., Reading, Mass., 1962.

late or extrapolate to find vapor-pressure values we have not measured, and perhaps cannot measure. Thus, for example, the procedure we have suggested for measuring vapor pressures cannot readily be carried far enough to determine a boiling point: i.e. the temperature at which the substance in question exerts a pressure of 760 mm. But we can easily extend the approximately straight line on a $\log P$ vs. $1/T$ plot, as shown in the figure, to determine the boiling temperature as that temperature for which $\log P = \log 760 = 2.881$.

To the degree that our experimental data fall on a straight line, we can represent them by the equation $\log P = A/T + B$, where A and B are empirically determinable constants characteristic of each substance. Furthermore, one can establish—on either theoretical or strictly empirical grounds—that term $A = -\Delta H/2.303R$. Here the minus sign signifies the negative slope of the $\log P$ vs. $1/T$ line, R is the familiar ideal-gas-law constant, 2.303 is the numerical factor by which we convert from natural logarithms to the denary logarithms we have used, and ΔH is the (empirically determinable) positive quantity of heat that must be added to vaporize one mole of the substance concerned. For a given substance, this heat of vaporization varies slightly from temperature to temperature, so that the A-term is not *quite* constant—producing the slight variation of slope that is principally responsible for a slight but observable curvature of a plot of empirical vapor-pressure data on axes of $\log P$ vs. $1/T$.

By now, no doubt, you will have thought several times: "What has all this to do with the determination of molecular formulas?" Be patient! We are getting there. From all the preceding material we wish to carry forward only a very simple and essentially empirical conclusion. No more than this: vapor pressure is a measurable property of a given substance and, when vapor pressures are graphed as $\log P$ vs. $1/T$, an approximately rectilinear plot is obtained.

The vapor pressure of solutions: Raoult's law. Where earlier we made vapor-pressure studies of pure solvents, let us study now *solutions* of various other materials in these solvents. We need make no change in the experimental approach sketched in Fig. 4–2—except that we must use a *large* excess of sample, in order that its concentration shall not change appreciably as the solvent vaporizes to different extents at different temperatures. But we do need to make a decision about the solutes to be used. Our ultimate goal is to develop a method by which the molecular weight of an *involatile* substance can be established, on the basis of measurable properties of its solution in a volatile solvent. In the development of any new method, however, it is obviously advantageous to try it first on some substance of known molecular weight. A reasonable choice of a test solute, then, meets these two specifications: (i) it should be volatile at high temperatures so that its molecular weight can be established by vapor-density work and (ii) it should be essentially involatile at the temperatures at which we propose to measure the solvent's vapor pressures, so that under these conditions it will behave like the involatile solutes that are our primary interest. Many such test substances are available. Naphthalene ($C_{10}H_8$), for example, boils at 280°C but can be handled at temperatures below 100°C as a largely involatile material. For concreteness, then, let us consider the behavior of solutions of naphthalene in benzene (boiling point of benzene: 80°C).

We measure the vapor pressure of pure benzene as a function of temperature and go on to measure the vapor pressure of benzene over some particular solution of naphthalene in benzene. The results obtained approximate those shown in Fig. 4–5. The two lines are very nearly parallel—indicating, we say, that the heat of vaporization of benzene from the solution is much the same as its heat of vaporization from pure benzene. [*Query:* What is the basis for this inference?] Note, however, that the line for the solution lies *below* that for the pure solvent. If we go on to make further trials with benzene solutions containing higher concentrations of naphthalene, the lines for the various solutions remain roughly parallel to that for pure benzene, but lie farther below it the more concentrated the solution concerned. Can we find some analytical expression relating the displacement of the vapor pressure line to the concentration of the solution concerned? Such an expression was discovered by Raoult, in the late 19th century, and reads

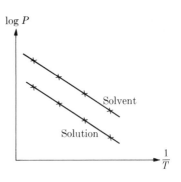

Figure 4–5

$$P = P^0 X_v.$$

Here P represents the vapor pressure of solvent over the solution, P^0 the vapor pressure of the pure solvent at the *same temperature*, and X_v the mole fraction of the solvent in the solution. From the kinetic-molecular point of view, this equation is not at all implausible. Certainly if we reduce the fraction of solvent molecules in the condensed phase, from $\frac{1}{1}$ (in the pure solvent) to some lower value X_v, it is hardly surprising that the vapor pressure developed by the solvent over the solution should be reduced to the fraction X_v of the vapor pressure over the pure solvent.

If the above equation could be written only for solutions of naphthalene in benzene, it would have little interest. But the equation gives promise of greater generality. Observe that it refers explicitly only to the mole fraction of the *solvent*, and surely we can bring the solvent to any desired mole fraction by the addition of quite different solutes, provided they are sufficiently soluble. As a matter of fact, experiment shows that the above equation is also applicable, with reasonable accuracy, to solutions made by dissolving in benzene any of a great number of other solutes that, like naphthalene, have known molecular weights. Making trials with such solutes in solvents other than benzene—and of course, using the values of P^0 appropriate to the particular solvent and temperature in question— we find that (with the notable exception of certain "ionizing solvents" like water) the *same* equation still holds good. Raoult's law, the equation $P = P^0 X_v$, is thus a *general* relation, applicable to any of a great variety of solvents. With this law in hand, we are at last in a position to determine the molecular weights of solutes that are *not* sufficiently volatile to permit the use of a vapor-density method. Before examining how such determinations can be made, we pause a moment to consider briefly (i) the possibility of still further generalizing Raoult's law and (ii) the extent to which we can rely on Raoult's law in our further studies.

First the generalization: We have considered only solutions of involatile solutes in volatile solvents, because only such solutions are relevant to our primary endeavor. However, we should not leave the impression that Raoult's law is restricted to the particular group of solutions that happens to be important to us. Imagine a solution made up by mixing two volatile components, A and B. If we regard A as the solvent, we will write for it

$$p_A = P_A^0 X_A$$

while if, instead, we regard B as the solvent, we will write

$$p_B = P_B^0 X_B.$$

Dalton's law of partial pressures makes it reasonable to suppose that the total pressure (P_T) over the solution is the sum of p_A and p_B. In this case we will have

$$P_T = P_A^0 X_A + P_B^0 X_B.$$

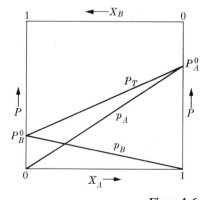

We can easily investigate the validity of this expression: our vapor-pressure technique does measure the *total* pressure to which the equation refers. In fact, we find that this equation is confirmed by a good many investigations in which, *at a given temperature*, one examines a series of specimens ranging from pure A through all intermediate concentrations to pure B (see Fig. 4–6). At one end of the range $(X_B = 1)$, the

Figure 4–6

observed pressure is simply the vapor pressure of pure B, P_B^0; at the other end of the range ($X_A = 1$), the observed pressure is simply the vapor pressure of pure A, P_A^0. At all intermediate concentrations the measured total pressures fall fairly well on the straight line drawn between P_A^0 and P_B^0—*which is just what Raoult's law predicts.** We have then no hesitation in drawing the additional lines, p_A and p_B, to represent the (unmeasured but not in principle unmeasurable) individual partial pressures of the two components.

We come then to what is for us the most important question: How heavily can we rely on Raoult's law? Like the gas laws (and most other such empirical regularities), Raoult's law is rigorously applicable only to certain ideal systems, and is but an approximation as applied to real systems, i.e. real solutions. Real gases at reasonably low pressures are excellently approximated as ideal gases: the great tenuity of the gas ensures that, on the average, the particles are so far removed from one another that there is little scope for the action of intermolecular forces assumed wholly absent in an ideal gas. But while real gases are thus well approximated as ideal, real solutions present a very different case. Here the component particles are closely packed together; there is then ample scope for the action of intermolecular forces that may perturb ideal behavior. A real solution well approximated by Raoult's ideal-solution law is, in fact, much less often encountered than a real gas well approximated by the ideal gas laws. We must then consider how we will be able to recognize those solutions to which Raoult's law applies with accuracy sufficient for our purposes.

Considering some particular solute-solvent pair, we have only to measure, at a *single* temperature, the vapor pressures over solutions in which the proportion of the two components is systematically varied. Assuming that the solute is an involatile substance completely miscible with the (volatile) solvent, the data obtained may fall on any curve like those shown in Fig. 4–7.† If the solution is sub-

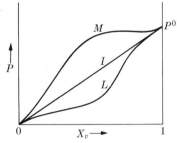

Figure 4–7

---

* Observe that the last equation can be rewritten in the form $P_T = P_A^0 X_A + P_B^0(1 - X_A) = (P_A^0 - P_B^0)X_A + P_B^0$. At a given temperature, P_A^0 and P_B^0 are constant, so that this is the equation of a straight line passing through P_A^0 when $X_A = 1$ and through P_B^0 when $X_B = 1$.

† Similar aberrations are, of course, found also when both compounds are volatile, and would show up in similar vagaries of the lines drawn in Fig. 4–6, which thus refers only to the case of an *ideal* solution.

stantially ideal, we will indeed find what Raoult's law predicts: the straight line (I) rising from $P = 0$ when $X_v = 0$, through $P = \frac{1}{2}P^0$ when $X_v = \frac{1}{2}$, to $P = P^0$ when $X_v = 1$ in the pure solvent. However, many solutions yield data falling on some line like M, or some line like L.

The line M is said to represent a *positive* deviation from Raoult's law: i.e. the observed vapor pressure is **more** than predicted. On our kinetic hypothesis we may interpret this deviation in terms of a difference in the intermolecular forces acting between solvent molecules on the one hand and between solvent and solute molecules on the other. Consider first a solution in which the second force is *weaker* than the first. From such a solution a solvent molecule, surrounded by a *mixture* of solute and solvent molecules, is (other things being equal) able to make its escape more easily than we would predict on the basis of studies of the pure solvent—where each solvent molecule is completely surrounded by others of its own kind. Thus the solvent vapor pressure over the solution is larger than predicted from Raoult's law. Consider, on the other hand, a solution in which the force of interaction between solvent and solute molecules is greater than the corresponding force between solvent molecules. From this solution a solvent molecule escapes less readily than we would predict on the basis of the behavior of the pure solvent. The solvent vapor pressure over such a solution is then less than would be predicted on the basis of Raoult's law— and we find the negative deviation indicated by line L. But once again this kind of hypothetical explanation is wholly irrelevant to our main purpose, which requires only that we note two points relating to Fig. 4–7.

First: If we propose to use Raoult's law in a determination of molecular weight (and, thence, molecular formula), small deviations from ideal behavior can easily be taken in stride. Just as in vapor-density work, only an approximate molecular weight is required for an accurate assignment of molecular formula. However, we should take care to avoid any use of a solution manifesting *gross* positive or negative deviations from Raoult's law. Such a solution can easily be recognized by measurement of its vapor pressure as a function of temperature. Large positive or negative deviations from Raoult's law must, our kinetic hypothesis suggests, imply molar heats of vaporization (of solvent from solution) that are significantly less or greater, respectively, than the heat of vaporization of solvent from pure solvent. Hence the *slope* of the log P vs. $1/T$ plot for the solution will not be the same as the slope of the corresponding plot for pure solvent. If in fact the two lines do diverge substantially from parallelism, we are thereby alerted to the conspicuous nonideality of a solution which we must *not*, then, use for a determination of the molecular weight of the solute.

The second point is in some sense complementary to the first. Observe that both the lines M and L converge on (and ultimately coincide with) the ideal line I at values of $X_v \rightarrow 1$, i.e. in the highly dilute solutions that possess the correspondingly low value of X_u $(= 1 - X_v) \to 0$. On our kinetic hypothesis, this is only to be expected. In highly dilute solutions each solvent molecule is almost entirely surrounded by other molecules of its own species, very much as it is in the pure solvent. Escape of a solvent molecule from the solution then requires neither more nor less energy than the escape from pure solvent, so that Raoult's law should apply excellently. Over what concentration range will the data for a real solution fall on the ideal-solution line expressing Raoult's law? Everything depends on the extent to which the forces of interaction between solute and solvent molecules approximate the forces between solvent molecules alone. The better the approximation, the more extensive will be the convergence of the real-solution line on the ideal-solution line. And we can *always* apply Raoult's law, with real confidence, to the solvent in a very highly dilute solution. This is exactly analogous to our previous observation that, as we proceed toward very low gas pressures, the ideal-gas laws apply to a real gas with increasing rigor, and with complete rigor at the limit $P \to 0$. Just so, at high dilutions the application of Raoult's law to the solvents in real solutions becomes increasingly rigorous, and completely rigorous in the limit $X_u \to 0$ or $X_v \to 1$. To conduct our determinations of molecular weight at very high dilutions is a goal approachable only over very serious experimental difficulties, but clearly it *is* the goal at which we should aim.

Molecular weights (and formulas) from measurements of vapor-pressure lowering. Given Raoult's law, it becomes very simple in principle to establish the molecular formulas we seek. We have only to measure the vapor pressure of solvent over a solution that contains a known weight of the involatile solute we wish to characterize. Comparing this vapor pressure with the (known or measurable) vapor pressure of the pure solvent at the same temperature, we use Raoult's law to determine the mole fraction of solvent in the solution. With this value in hand, we easily find the mole fraction of solute present, whence we readily establish the number of *moles* of solute that correspond to the known *weight* of solute used. We can then conclude the determination exactly as we did in our use of vapor-density data: see p. 106. An illustrative problem will help consolidate this abstract analysis.

Illustrative Example. In a lecture demonstration conducted at room temperature, pure acetone was injected into the bottom of a barometer. Into a second barometer (originally standing at the same level as the first) was injected a large excess of a solution containing 30 gm of naphthalene in 100 gm of acetone. When equilibrium was reached after the injections, the mercury in the first barometer stood 200 mm below its original level, while the mercury in the second barometer stood 175 mm below its original level. Given that the empirical formula of naphthalene is $(C_5H_4)_x$ and that the molecular weight of acetone is 58, calculate the molecular formula of naphthalene.

At the working temperature the vapor pressure of the pure solvent (P^0) is 200 mm; the vapor pressure of solvent over the solution (P) is 175 mm. Thus we can write

$$X_v = \frac{P}{P^0} = \frac{175}{200} = \frac{7}{8} \quad \text{and} \quad X_u = 1 - X_v = \frac{1}{8}.$$

Let n represent the (unknown) moles of solute present. We have then

$$X_u = \frac{\text{moles naphthalene}}{\text{moles naphthalene} + \text{moles acetone}} = \frac{n}{n + 100/58}.$$

Therefore

$$\frac{n}{n + 100/58} = \frac{1}{8},$$

whence

$$8n = n + \frac{100}{58} \quad \text{and} \quad n = \frac{100}{(7)(58)} = 0.25.$$

Knowing that 30 gm of naphthalene represent approximately 0.25 mole, we can establish the approximate molecular weight (M) of naphthalene:

$$\frac{30}{M} \doteq 0.25 \quad \text{or} \quad M \doteq \frac{30}{0.25} = 120.$$

But in the light of the known empirical formula, $(C_5H_4)_x$, only certain values of molecular weight are at all permissible:

$$M = x[5(12) + 4(1)] = 64x.$$

Comparing the last two equations, we see that $x = 2$, that the molecular formula is then $C_{10}H_8$, and that the accurate molecular weight is 128. This result is confirmed by the formula assignable to naphthalene by vapor-density studies at a much higher temperature. The result obtained in this lecture demonstration was fortuitously good—far better than one has any right to expect from work with so concentrated a solution. Observe, however, that given the small-whole-number restriction under which we operate, even a much cruder experimental value for M would be quite sufficient for an unequivocal assignment of molecular formula.

A more tedious but intrinsically more accurate mode of operation entirely eliminates the difficult determination of vapor pressure as such. A very simple indirect approach turns the trick. When air (or any other gas) is passed into the right arm of the "saturator" sketched in Fig. 4–8, the gas

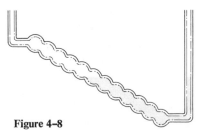

Figure 4–8

bubbles through a lengthy column of the volatile solvent present in the saturator and leaves the left arm fully laden with solvent at its equilibrium vapor pressure. Let us now perform an experiment using *two* matched saturators: one we charge with pure solvent, the other with a solution, in the same solvent, of the involatile solute in which we are interested. We weigh both saturators, and place them in a well-stirred thermostat. A slow, metered stream of air is drawn through each saturator *separately*, and this operation is continued until an equal number of liters of gas has passed through each saturator. The saturators are then withdrawn from the thermostat and reweighed to determine the amount of solvent evaporated from each. Having passed the same volume of air through each saturator, we can take the ratio of the respective weight losses to represent also the ratio of the respective vapor pressures. [*Query:* Why?] Since the saturators functioned at the same temperature, this ratio of vapor pressures can at once be substituted in Raoult's law:

$$X_v = \frac{P}{P^0} = \frac{\text{weight loss from solution}}{\text{weight loss from solvent}}.$$

With X_v thus established, the calculation of molecular formulas can follow exactly the same course displayed in the last illustrative example.

When we actually determine the vapor-pressure lowering (whether directly, or indirectly as above) we are debarred from working with the highly dilute solutions to which Raoult's law is applicable with greatest rigor—for over such solutions the vapor pressure differs only minutely from that over the pure solvent. This difficulty is surmounted by an ingenious approach using only the simple apparatus sketched in Fig. 4–9. We weigh each of the two broad flat dishes. Into one we put a weighed sample of our involatile unknown substance (Q); into the other we put a comparable weight of an involatile substance (K) whose molecular weight is already known to us. To each dish we add some (indeterminate) quantity of the same volatile solvent. We cap the assembly with a bell jar and set it aside for some days in an enclosure maintained at a uniform temperature. Now Raoult's law makes it clear that, if the mole fraction of solvent is not the same in both solutions, the vapor pressure produced by the solution with the greater mole fraction of solvent will be greater than the vapor pressure over the other solution.
Hence vapor from the first solution will pass over and condense in the second. But as this transfer continues, the mole fraction of solvent in the first solution will be progressively reduced, and the mole fraction of solvent in the second solution will be progressively increased.

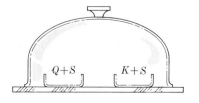

Figure 4–9

At last the mole fraction of solvent in both solutions must reach the same value. The vapor pressure of solvent over both the solutions is then the same, and no further net redistribution of solvent will take place. When this state of equilibrium is achieved, we remove the bell jar, immediately cap the two dishes, and reweigh them to determine the weight of solvent that each contains. The calculation is then perfectly straightforward. If we symbolize by S_K and S_Q the number of moles of solvent associated, at equilibrium, with K and Q, respectively, and by n_K and n_Q the number of moles of K and Q present, we can write

$$\frac{S_Q}{S_Q + n_Q} = X_v = \frac{S_K}{S_K + n_K},$$
$$S_Q S_K + S_Q n_K = S_Q S_K + n_Q S_K,$$
$$n_Q = \frac{S_Q}{S_K} n_K.$$

The ratio S_Q/S_K is simply the ratio of the weights of solvent in the two respective dishes when equilibrium is reached. (*Observe:* We don't even have to know the molecular weight of the solvent, since the *ratio* of solvent moles is necessarily the same as the *ratio* of solvent weights.) The value of n_K is of course known, for we have used a known weight of a substance K whose molecular weight is also known. Hence, the above equation can at once be solved for the only unknown in it: n_Q. With n_Q so established, and knowing the weight of Q used, we proceed as usual to determine an approximate molecular weight, etc. This truly elegant method of "isothermal distillation" is operable at relatively high dilutions and yields results of excellent quality.

Raoult's law as such does not always offer the most *convenient* approach to determination of molecular weights. But it is the fundamental relation underlying other approaches to which we turn in a moment. First, however, we pause to consider how Raoult's law can be recast in several forms that will later prove useful to us. One such re-expression is easily obtained by writing

$$P = P^0 X_v = P^0(1 - X_u) = P^0 - P^0 X_u.$$

Therefore

$$P^0 X_u = P^0 - P = \Delta P,$$

where ΔP is the actual vapor-pressure lowering, i.e. the margin by which the vapor pressure of the solution (P) fails to come up to the vapor pressure of the pure solvent (P^0). Thus we can write Raoult's law in the form

$$X_u = \Delta P/P^0.$$

Observe further that if we deal with *very* dilute solutions, we can approximate the unwieldy mole fraction in terms of the molality of the solute, $m \doteq 1000X_u/M_{\text{solvent}}$. We then obtain

$$\frac{\Delta P}{P^0} = X_u \doteq \frac{M_{\text{solvent}}}{1000} \cdot m \qquad \text{or} \qquad \Delta P \doteq \left[\frac{P^0 M_{\text{solvent}}}{1000}\right] m.$$

The bracketed expression is composed solely of terms referring to the solvent. Hence, for a given solvent at a given temperature, we can replace the bracketed expression by a single "molal vapor-pressure constant" (K_V). Then

$$\Delta P = K_V m.$$

This strikingly simple equation—applicable only to very dilute solutions —brings out a crucial point. The magnitude of ΔP depends on the nature of the solvent (since K_V will clearly be different for different solvents) and on the concentration of the solute. But *the observed vapor-pressure lowering is completely independent of the nature of the solute.*[*] As a sharply contrasting case, note that the viscosity of a solution in a given solvent *is* very heavily dependent on the identity of the solute: from viscosimetric measurements we *cannot* infer the number of moles of solute present. However, from the observed value of ΔP we *can* infer the number of moles of dissolved substance present, whatever may be the identity of that solute. The possibility of making this inference is what invests with importance both Raoult's law and the other colligative properties now to be considered.

The Boiling-Point Elevation (ΔT_B) and Freezing-Point Depression (ΔT_F)

Raoult's law requires that, at *every* temperature, the vapor pressure of a solution of an involatile solute be less than the vapor pressure of the corresponding pure solvent at the same temperature. Hence a solution must have a boiling point higher than that of its solvent and a freezing point lower than that of its solvent. By definition, the boiling point of a liquid is that temperature at which it exerts a vapor pressure of 760 mm. At the normal boiling point (T_B) of the pure solvent, the solution exerts some vapor pressure (given by Raoult's law) less than 760 mm. Consequently, the vapor pressure of the solution will reach 760 mm only at some temperature (T_B^*) higher than T_B by the margin of ΔT_B, where $\Delta T_B \equiv T_B^* - T_B$ (see Fig. 4–10). Looking then to the other end of the scale, we identify the freezing point of the pure solvent as that temperature at which liquid and solid solvent stand together at equilibrium. Such equilibrium

---

[*] Observe that this statement applies also to the general form of Raoult's law, applicable at higher concentrations: $\Delta P = [P^0]X_u$. The bracketed term refers to the pure solvent only, and the X_u-term refers only to the concentration of the solute and *not to its identity.*

demands equality of vapor pressures: otherwise, if only by the mechanism of isothermal distillation we have just discussed, one phase would grow at the expense of the other. The freezing point of the pure solvent (T_F) is thus assignable as that temperature at which the vapor pressure lines for liquid and solid solvent intersect. At the normal freezing point of the pure solvent, however, the solution exerts a vapor pressure less than that required for equilibrium with the pure solid solvent. The vapor-pressure line for the solution intersects the vapor-pressure line of the pure solid only at some temperature (T_F^*) lower than T_F. (*Example:* When alcohol is added to the water in a car radiator, ice does not begin to deposit until some temperature lower than 273°K.) We symbolize the positive magnitude of the freezing point depression as ΔT_F, and define it by the equation $\Delta T_F \equiv T_F - T_F^*$.

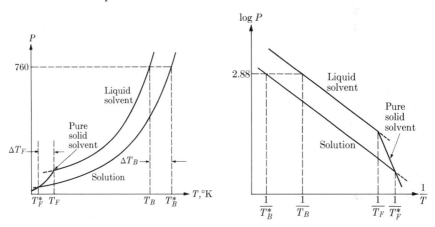

Figure 4–10   **Figure 4–11**

When we replot the data graphed above, now on the axes $\log P$ vs. $1/T$, our data fall on approximately straight lines (Fig. 4–11), and it is obvious in principle that we can use Raoult's law to calculate the actual magnitudes of ΔT_B and ΔT_F. The essentially straightforward but rather tedious exercise in analytic geometry required to obtain expressions for ΔT_B and ΔT_F is fully set forth in Appendix I. For *very dilute solutions*, the results so obtained are

$$\Delta T_B = \left[\frac{RT_B^2 M}{1000 \cdot \Delta H_V}\right] m, \qquad \Delta T_F = \left[\frac{RT_B^2 M}{1000 \cdot \Delta H_F}\right] m.$$

In these symmetric expressions m represents the molality of solute in the solution manifesting boiling-point elevation ΔT_B and freezing-point depression ΔT_F. Here R is the ubiquitous ideal-gas-law constant, T_B and T_F are, respectively, the boiling point and freezing point of the pure *solvent*, and M represents the molecular weight of the *solvent*. By ΔH_V we symbolize the molar heat of vaporization of the *solvent:* recall that the slope of the vapor-pressure lines for solvent and for ideal solution is given as $-\Delta H_V/2.3R$. And ΔH_F symbolizes the molar heat of fusion of the solid *solvent:* this term reflects the difference in the slopes of the vapor-pressure lines for the solution and for the pure solid solvent.*

The detailed make-up of the complex expressions within the brackets is of far less importance to us than one simple qualitative observation: *All the terms within the brackets are either invariant (R and 1000) or constants characteristic of the solvent alone.* Nowhere within the brackets are there terms reflecting the identity of the solute. Thus, for *all* ideal solutions made up in any given solvent, the value of the bracketed expressions should be constants wholly independent of the identity of the solutes concerned. We can then drastically simplify the above expressions by writing

$$\Delta T_B = K_B m, \qquad \Delta T_F = K_F m.$$

Here K_B is the so-called boiling-point-elevation constant, indifferently applicable to solutions of *any* solute in a given solvent. And similarly, K_F is the freezing-point-depression constant, dependent only on the identity of the solvent. Only the last two simple equations will figure in our further inquiry. Bear in mind that both these expressions (like the analogous simplified expression of Raoult's law) are restricted to use with *very dilute solutions.* If the solution in question is more concentrated than ca. $0.05\,m$, the corresponding equations in terms of mole fraction (see Appendix I) should be used.

To determine the values of K_B and K_F, one can proceed by the same experimental method later to be used in applying the equations. In this case, we need only add to the solvent in question a known concentration of some solute whose molecular weight is already known to us. Measuring the actual magnitudes of ΔT_B and ΔT_F for the solution of known solute molality (m), we can readily calculate K_B and K_F by way of the above equations. By this use of solutes having known molecular weights, we can in effect "calibrate" the solvent. For, with the values of K_B and K_F so obtained, we can proceed to apply our equations to solutions of solutes to which molecular weights have *not* earlier been assigned. Observe that when

---

* We must stress an important special restriction on the validity of the freezing-point-depression equation. That equation is derived on the *assumption* that the vapor-pressure line of the solid phase, in equilibrium with the solution, is identical with the vapor-pressure line of the pure solid solvent. This assumption is obviously vulnerable if the solid in question is not pure solvent but, instead, a solid solution of solute in solvent. Thus the freezing-point-depression equation will be applicable only to those solutions from which pure solid solvent is the first solid that separates when the solution is cooled.

TABLE 4–1

Solvent	K_B		K_F	
	calculated	measured	calculated	measured
Water	0.513	0.51	1.86	1.86
Benzene	2.63	2.6	5.07	5.12
Chloroform	3.78	3.9	4.7	4.9
Carbon tetrachloride	5.22	4.9	32.	30.

K_B and K_F are established empirically, as indicated, we need rely on theory only for what empiricism can readily confirm: the proposition that for a given solvent, K_B and K_F *are* constants irrespective of the solute concerned. But we can of course also make a theoretical calculation of K_B and K_F—simply by substituting appropriate figures for the solvent parameters appearing in the bracketed expressions that K_B and K_F represent. And the impressive agreement of the *measured* and the *calculated* values of K_B and K_F, shown in Table 4–1, then constitutes strong evidence that our theory is in fact quite sound.

Molecular weights from measurements of ΔT_B and ΔT_F. Historically, boiling-point and freezing-point methods have offered an important route to the determination of molecular formulas. These methods yield results in only a fraction of the time required by the method of isothermal distillation. Moreover, it is fundamentally easier to measure a small temperature difference (which is all that is required for use of these methods) than to measure a small lowering of vapor pressure.

For a determination of ΔT_B, one may use the Cottrell apparatus shown in Fig. 4–12. Into the vertical tube one dispenses a solution containing a known weight of the solute of interest, in a known weight of a solvent for which the value of K_B has earlier been established. The tube is then heated from the bottom. When the solution has come to a boil, the percolator-like insertion drenches the bulb of the thermometer with a mixture of liquid and vapor at the boiling-point of the solution, which can then be read off from the thermometer. The difference between this temperature and the boiling temperature of the pure solvent (measured earlier with the same apparatus) represents ΔT_B.

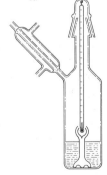

Figure 4–12

For a determination of ΔT_F, one prepares, in a thin walled tube about 2 mm in diameter, a small amount of a mixture containing a known weight of the solute of interest and a known weight of a (solid) solvent for which the value of K_F is known. One melts this mixture, running it down to the bottom of the tube, where it will resolidify. The tube is then so attached to a thermometer that the sample lies immediately beside the thermometer bulb. The assembly is inserted in a well-stirred heating bath, the temperature of which is very gradually increased. The material in the capillary tube melts over a considerable range of temperature. Why? Because the melt at first produced will contain all the solute but only a fraction of the solvent, most of which will still be present in solid form. In the comparatively concentrated solution thus produced, the solute molality (m) is large and, therefore, ΔT_F $(= K_F m)$ must also be large. But, as more and more of the solid solvent is melted, m becomes smaller and so too must ΔT_F. What then shall we take as *the* temperature of interest? We record, as the melting point, *only* the temperature at which the last speck of solid disappears—for *that* speck will have melted in equilibrium with a liquid having essentially the bulk concentration of our weighed sample. The value of ΔT_F is then established by subtracting this melting point from the melting point of the pure solvent—which can be measured in the same experiment, by attaching to the thermometer another fine tube containing pure solvent.*

Having in hand methods for establishing ΔT_B and ΔT_F for solutions—methods competent also to establish K_B and K_F for solvents—we have only to show how these data permit the determination of the molecular formula of a solute for which we have only an empirical formula. The calculation is the same in either case, and will be illustrated only for a determination based on measurement of ΔT_F.

Illustrative Example. Alizarin is a naturally occurring dyestuff with empirical formula $(C_7H_5O)_x$; camphor melts at $+176.5°C$ and has for its molal freezing-point-depression constant the conspicuously high value $K_F = 40$. To 1.0 gm of camphor was added 0.01 gm of alizarin. In a melting-point determination made on a representative sample of this mixture, the last speck of solid camphor disappeared at $+174.5°C$. What is the molecular formula of alizarin?

The experiment establishes that $\Delta T_F = 2.0°$. Knowing K_F, we can easily establish the molality of the alizarin in the solution:

$$m = \frac{\Delta T_F}{K_F} = \frac{2.0}{40} = 0.05.$$

---

* We spoke of a *freezing*-point depression; yet here we speak of *melting* points. The distinction raises no real difficulty. When a speck of solid solvent stands in equilibrium with a solution, *the equilibrium temperature must be the same* whether this is the *first* speck of solid to appear as the system is *cooled* (in a determination of freezing point) or the *last* speck of solid to disappear as the system is *heated* (in a determination of melting point). Ordinarily we prefer measurements of melting point to measurements of freezing point because, though solids cannot be superheated, liquids can be supercooled—with consequent production of deceptive nonequilibrium states.

This molality represents the number of moles of alizarin per 1000 gm of solvent (camphor); but we used only 1.0 gm of camphor in preparing the solution. Hence the number of moles of alizarin actually present (n) must be one-thousandth of the observed molality. That is,

$$n = m \frac{1}{1000} = \frac{0.05}{1000} = 5 \times 10^{-5}.$$

The rest is completely familiar. Knowing that 0.01 gm of alizarin represents 5×10^{-5} mole of alizarin, we easily approximate its molecular weight (M) as

$$\frac{0.01}{M} \doteq 5 \times 10^{-5} \quad \text{and} \quad M = \frac{1}{0.005} = 200.$$

Given also the empirical formula of alizarin, we know that its accurate molecular weight can be expressed as

$$M = x[7(12) + 5(1) + 1(16)] = 105x.$$

We can then at once write $C_{14}H_{10}O_2$ as the molecular formula of alizarin.

Osmotic Pressure and Its Use in Determining Molecular Weights

The colligative-property methods so far discussed suffice to establish approximate molecular weights for the great majority of substances to which we wish to assign molecular formulas. One group of substances, however, demands a procedure beyond any so far mentioned. In this group we find the enormous polymeric molecules of such great interest to biochemists. For many such substances we do not now have even empirical formulas and hence cannot hope to assign molecular formulas at present. But we may still hope to gain some idea of the molecular magnitudes involved— from determinations of the molecular weights of these substances. This undertaking presents great difficulties. Many of these substances are only sparingly soluble and, in any case, their gigantic molecular weights (ranging up into the millions) make it quite impossible to prepare substantially concentrated solutions of them. The solute molalities being minute, the vapor-pressure lowerings, boiling-point elevations, or freezing-point depressions are then much too small to be readily measured. By use of very exacting techniques, these quantities may in some cases be established with sufficient accuracy to permit at least a rough estimate of molecular weight. But it would be highly desirable to have a simple method capable of yielding good results in all such cases.

The phenomenon of osmotic pressure materializes whenever a solution and the corresponding pure solvent interact through a membrane selectively permeable to solvent molecules but not to solute molecules. Many such semipermeable membranes are known: cellophane will often work quite well. The actual mechanism underlying this selective permeability remains very much in doubt—particularly in regard to the many selectively permeable membranes that play so large a role in living biochemical systems. But for our present purpose we can entirely pass over the doubtful causal mechanism and focus only on its demonstrable effects. A semipermeable membrane freely passes small solvent molecules but is substantially impermeable to large solute molecules.* Suppose that we fit such a membrane across the middle of a tube like that shown in Fig. 4–13, dividing it into two chambers, each of which is fitted with a length of fine capillary tubing. We fill the left chamber with a solvent to which the membrane is permeable; we fill the right chamber with a dilute solution, in the same solvent, of some substance to which the membrane is impermeable. If we start with the liquid levels at the same height in the two capillaries, we find that the system is *not* at equilibrium. From the observed displacement of the liquid levels, we infer that there is a net transfer of solvent across the membrane, from the pure-solvent side to the solution side. That is, the solvent passes from where it is more concentrated (in the pure solvent $X_v = 1$) to where it is less concentrated (in the solution $X_v < 1$). In itself, such a transfer is perhaps not very surprising. But we find further that this migration of solvent continues only until the liquid levels in the capillaries differ by some particular height (h) which is characteristic of the composition of the solution and the temperature of operation. To this height differential corresponds a hydrostatic pressure we symbolize as π, and call the "osmotic pressure" of the solution concerned. To express this pressure in centimeters of mercury, we need only use the simple equation $\pi = (\rho/13.5)h$, where ρ is the density of the solution ($\doteq 1$ for very dilute *aqueous* solutions) and 13.5 stands for the density of mercury.

To avoid serious dilution of the solution of known composition with which we begin, we may use a rather large membrane-chamber and very fine capillaries. The osmotic pressure that prevents any further net transfer of solvent is then established as soon as a very minute amount of solvent has passed into the very large volume of solution—leaving the composition of this solution essentially unchanged. Alternatively, we can estimate the volume of solvent transferred (from the measurable extent of the decline of solvent level in the left-hand capillary) and calculate the *final* concentration of the solution after it has thus been diluted. But these are only small

---

* This selectivity may fail when the two species of molecule are comparable in size. As a result, it is difficult to determine, by osmotic-pressure measurements, the molecular weights of substances consisting of *small* molecules. However, for such substances we already have an ample battery of methods. It is the substances with *large* molecules that still present a challenge to us, and the problem of membrane selectivity is least troublesome for precisely these substances.

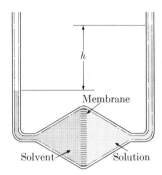

Figure 4–13

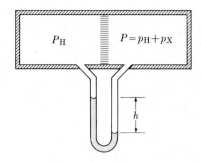

Figure 4–14

matters of practical detail, and we must now come to grips with a major question of principle. How is the osmotic pressure of a solution related to its concentration? Though, at first sight, we see no obvious way of approaching this problem, we may follow a plausible line of analogic reasoning first proposed by van't Hoff in the late 19th century. After all, we *have* already considered a situation at least remotely analogous to that now confronting us.

In our discussion of the kinetic theory, we encountered (p. 45) a membrane semipermeable to gases, as palladium is permeable to hydrogen but not to other gases. Suppose we fit such a membrane to a system like that shown in Fig. 4–14. Into the left chamber we introduce some particular pressure (P_H) of pure hydrogen; into the right chamber, an exactly equal total pressure (P) of a *mixture* of hydrogen with some gas X to which the membrane is impermeable. Initially the manometer levels stand at the same height (since $P = P_H$), but this is not an equilibrium situation. The pressure of hydrogen on the left is necessarily greater than the partial pressure (p_H) of hydrogen on the right, for $p_H = P - p_X = P_H - p_X < P_H$. As expected, we find a net transfer of hydrogen from the left (where it is more concentrated) to the right (where it is less concentrated)— with consequent change of the manometer levels. An unchanging state of equilibrium will be reached only when the hydrogen pressure on both sides of the membrane has become the same, i.e. when $P_H = p_H$. At this point the manometer will show some unchanging difference of height h. To what does this pressure differential (ω) correspond? With the hydrogen pressures equal on both sides of the membrane, the pressure differential can arise only through the presence of component X—exerting its own partial pressure (p_X) in the right chamber but completely absent from the chamber on the left. Let us denote by n_X the number of moles of X present in the right chamber and by c the "molar concentration" of X—that is, the number of moles of component X per liter of volume on the right. A very interesting question now arises. Had we no prior knowledge of the number of moles of X introduced into the right chamber, and no knowledge of its volume (V), could we still infer the concentration c by measurement of the pressure differential ω? The answer is, of course, "Yes"—provided that we know the temperature of the system. For our ideal gas law tells us that

$$p_X V = n_X RT.$$

But p_X, we saw, is identical with the measured pressure differential ω, so that we can write

$$\omega V = n_X RT.$$

For the molar concentration (c) we can write

$$c = n_X / V.$$

Therefore

$$\omega = cRT.$$

Throughout the above paragraph we stressed the points of resemblance between the system involving a membrane selectively permeable to one component of a gas mixture and the osmotic system involving a membrane selectively permeable to one component of a solution. Clearly there are many points of resemblance and, **if** in fact these systems are analogous, we may hope to apply to the osmotic system the same equation worked out for a system of gases. That is a very large **if**, and today the analogy is generally discounted. On the other hand, it is possible to develop (on a basis laid down in the next chapter) a convincing derivation of the *same* equation for osmotic systems—with the important qualification that the equation is then shown to be applicable only to extremely dilute solutions. This (essentially thermodynamic) derivation is outlined in Appendix II. But, ultimately, our present concern is quite independent of *any* derivation. For all such a derivation can tell us is that a certain empirical regularity *should* occur; whether or not it *does* occur is a matter to be decided empirically. Once we have some indication of the *form* of the regularity we should seek (and even van't Hoff's analogical argument gives us this much), it is easy enough to put the proposed regularity to the test of experience. Let us do so.

We have available to us some substances possessing molecular weights low enough to be established with accuracy by the methods of vapor-pressure lowering, boiling-point elevation, and/or freezing-point depression, and yet high enough to ensure that these substances will not pass through osmotic membranes that readily pass small solvent molecules. We prepare solutions containing known molar concentrations of these substances, as solutes, in some chosen solvent(s). We determine the osmotic pressure developed by these solutions when they are brought in contact with the corresponding pure solvent through an osmotic membrane permeable only to the solvent. We then find that the simple osmotic-pressure relation, $\pi = cRT$, is in fact a quite satisfactory law *in the limit of very low solute concentrations.* Like all the gas laws, like all the other colligative-property laws, the osmotic-pressure law gives good results only at very low concentrations; but, unlike the other laws, it fails much sooner as concentrations are increased.* However, to get reasonably good results from this law, we have only to proceed as we did in the method of limiting gas densities. We there extrapolated, to the limit $P \rightarrow 0$, along a plot of δ/P vs. P constructed from gas-density data obtained at finite pressures. To obtain an analogous plot of osmotic-pressure data, we need only observe that in our osmotic-pressure equation, c stands for the moles of solute per liter. Letting w represent the (known) weight of solute per liter of solution, and letting M represent the (unknown) molecular weight of that solute, we can rewrite the osmotic-pressure equa-

tion as follows:

$$\pi = cRT = \frac{w}{M} RT,$$

whence it follows that

$$M = \frac{RT}{\pi/w}.$$

Experimental measurements supply a value of π corresponding to each finite concentration of solute. Thus we need only plot our data as the quotient π/w vs. w, as shown in Fig. 4–15, and extrapolate to the limit $w \rightarrow 0$ (i.e. infinite dilu-

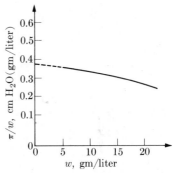

Figure 4–15

tion). Substituting, in the last equation, the limiting value of π/w established by this extrapolation, we can then calculate a quite respectably accurate value for the molecular weight of the solute concerned.

This mode of operation, well tested for smaller molecules of known molecular weight, can be extrapolated to determinations of molecular weights running into tens and hundreds of thousands. The results obtained are apparently sound. At least they are consistent with each other and, also, generally concordant with results obtained by an entirely independent method for determining such molecular weights, which is briefly noted in

---

* For a relation applicable to the osmotic pressures exerted by solutions with higher concentrations, see Appendix II.

Chapter 5. It remains then only to show how far this osmotic-pressure method surpasses the other colligative-property methods, as applied to materials of high molecular weight. This point can best be made clear with the aid of an illustrative example.

Illustrative Example. Apparatus similar to that shown in Fig. 4–13 was used to measure the osmotic pressure of aqueous solutions containing known weights of horse hemoglobin per liter of solution. The experiment was conducted at 298°K, and the pressures were expressed in centimeters of water height differential of the liquid levels in the two capillary tubes. The experimental results were plotted as shown in Fig. 4–15. The smallest osmotic pressure actually measured was the ca. 1.8 cm found with a solution containing 5 gm of hemoglobin per liter. What is the molecular weight of horse hemoglobin?

Noting that mercury is 13.5 times as dense as water, we convert the limiting value of π/w to centimeters of mercury:

$$\frac{\pi}{w} = \frac{1}{13.5}\,(0.37) \;=\; 0.0274 \text{ cm Hg/gm per liter.}$$

With pressure expressed in *cm Hg* and concentration in grams *per liter*, 6.23 liter-cm Hg/mole-°K will be the appropriate value for R when, as now, we substitute in the equation:

$$M = \frac{RT}{\pi/w} = \frac{(6.23)(298)}{0.0274} = 68,000.$$

The same result may be obtained in a much less elegant fashion that does, however, bring out the parallelism of this method with the other methods considered in the present chapter. Our limiting value of π/w expresses in effect the *ideal* value (0.0274 cm Hg) of the osmotic pressure shown by a solution containing 1 gm of hemoglobin per liter. By substitution in the equation $\pi = cRT$, we find that

$$0.0274 = c(6.23)(298) \qquad \text{or} \qquad c = 1.47 \times 10^{-5}.$$

We have here reached exactly the same position sought and attained in every earlier determination of molecular weight: we know the number of moles corresponding to a known weight of sample. And we can then go on, as before, to write

$$\frac{1.0}{M} = 1.47 \times 10^{-5} \qquad \text{or} \qquad M = 68,000.$$

Observe that to establish this very high molecular weight, we had only to measure differences of water level ranging upward from the 18 mm found with a solution containing 5 gm of hemoglobin per liter. Such measurements can readily be made with an accuracy of 1%. But in an attempt to determine the molecular weight by way of a measurement of freezing-point depression we would be confronted by a very different situation. The solution containing 5 gm of hemoglobin is dilute enough that its molality cannot differ significantly from its molarity $= 5.0/68,000 = 7 \times 10^{-5}$. Knowing that for water $K_F = 1.86$, we have

$$\Delta T_F = (1.86)(7 \times 10^{-5}) = 0.00013°C.$$

To measure a temperature difference of this magnitude, with sufficient accuracy to permit a meaningful determination of molecular weight, is no light undertaking—and obviously a matter of much greater difficulty than a reading of the pressure differential represented by an 18-mm column of water.

PROBLEMS

The following data may prove useful in the solution of the problems: atomic weights: H, 1; C, 12; O, 16; Si, 28; $R = 6.23$ liter-cm Hg/mole-°K; molar volume $= 22.4$ liters STP.

1. To fill a one-liter bulb to a pressure of 1.5 atm at 136.5°C, there are required 6.52 gm of a compound containing 38.4% silicon, 49.27% carbon, and 12.33% hydrogen. Determine the empirical formula, molecular weight, and molecular formula of the compound.

2. An organic hydrocarbon containing 14.3% hydrogen and 85.7% carbon is subjected to catalytic hydrogenation. It is known that two atoms of hydrogen are absorbed by each molecule of the hydrocarbon. It is found that 0.112 gm of the hydrocarbon absorbs 6.72 cc of hydrogen measured at 136.5°C and a pressure ten times normal atmospheric pressure. Compute the empirical formula, molecular weight, and molecular formula of the hydrocarbon.

3. Tartaric acid is an organic acid with empirical formula $C_2H_3O_3$. An aqueous solution containing 15 gm of tartaric acid per liter is titrated with a 0.15 M solution of NaOH. To titrate 30 ml of the tartaric-acid solution just 40 ml of the NaOH solution are required.

   (a) As a logical extension of the definition given on p. 4, we can define the equivalent weight of an acid as the number of grams of acid that yield 1.0 gm (or 1.0 mole) of titratably acidic hydrogen. What is the equivalent weight of tartaric acid?

   (b) Having found the equivalent weight of an acid, what additional information (or assumption) will permit one to assign the molecular weight of this acid?

   (c) The molecular weight of tartaric acid is actually 150. Comparing this with the equivalent weight calculated in (a), what conclusion can you draw about the qualitative nature of tartaric acid?

4. The method of isothermal distillation finds an elegantly simple expression in Signer's technique for the determination of molecular weights (see Fig. 4–16). Into bulb Q we introduce a known weight of the substance to be

characterized; into bulb K we introduce a known weight of some substance to which a molecular weight has already been assigned. An indeterminate weight of volatile solvent is added to both bulbs and—after removal, with a vacuum pump, of the bulk of the air present—the apparatus is sealed off and placed for some time in a uniform-temperature enclosure. Passage of solvent vapor

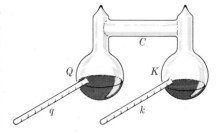

Figure 4–16

through the wide connecting tube (C) soon brings to equilibrium the broad, shallow pools of solution exposed in the two bulbs. The apparatus is then carefully rotated so that the solutions in Q and K are, respectively, drained into the two slender graduated tubes q and k, where the liquid volumes can easily be read off.

In an actual experiment, 0.1 gm of dibromobenzene (molecular weight, 236) was added to bulb K, and 0.1 gm of azobenzene to bulb Q. A large excess of volatile solvent was then added and, when equilibrium was at last established, the liquid volume read in tube k was 8.0 ml while that read in tube q was 10.0 ml.

(a) What (if any) additional data and/or assumptions must be used in deriving the molecular weight of azobenzene from the experimental data cited above?

(b) What is the apparent molecular weight of azobenzene?

(c) Why is it advantageous to remove the bulk of the air from the system? Why is it advantageous to equilibrate the system while the solutions stand in bulbs Q and K, and to read the volumes while the solutions stand in tubes q and k?

(d) In such a determination, how could one ascertain that the two solutions have actually reached equilibrium?

5. In using paired saturators to determine the vapor-pressure lowering for a solution, Ostwald suggested that—instead of connecting the saturators in parallel, as described on p. 120—one might do well to connect them in series. With both saturators held in the same thermostat, one passes some indeterminate volume of air *first* through the solution, *then* through the corresponding pure solvent, and one measures the loss of weight thus produced in each saturator.

(a) Letting w_1 and w_2 represent the weight losses of the first and second saturators respectively, demonstrate that

$$\frac{\Delta P}{P^0} = \frac{w_2}{w_1 + w_2}.$$

(b) In an actual experiment, dry air was drawn first through a saturator charged with a 10% solution of urea in water and then through a saturator charged with pure water. The first saturator lost 0.625 gm; the second lost 0.021 gm. Assuming that urea is involatile, and taking 18 as the molecular weight of water, calculate the approximate molecular weight of urea.

(c) Other things being equal, why might one prefer the use of saturators in series rather than in parallel as described on p. 120?

6. When 0.001 mole of substance Q was dissolved in a little water, 2.00 gm of a solution containing 10.9 weight % Q was obtained. On measurement, the vapor pressure of this solution was found to be 3.5 mm of mercury less than that of water at the same temperature. Given that for water the equation $\log P = -2255/T + 8.941$ expresses the dependence of the vapor pressure (P, in mm Hg) on absolute temperature (T), determine the temperature at which the vapor pressure measurement was made. Also, calculate the molecular weight of substance Q, using 18 as the molecular weight of water.

7. A compound X is known to consist only of carbon, hydrogen, and oxygen. When 0.72 gm of X is burned with excess oxygen, there are obtained 0.36 gm of water and sufficient carbon dioxide to react with 60 ml of $0.5M$ $Ba(OH)_2$, according to the reaction

$$Ba(OH)_2 + CO_2 = BaCO_3 + H_2O.$$

When 0.0072 gm of compound X is dissolved in 1 gm of camphor, the freezing point of the solution is found to be 172°C. Calculate the empirical formula, molecular weight, and molecular formula of compound X. (For camphor, the freezing point is 176°C; the molal freezing-point-depression constant is 40.)

8. When to 1 mole of the solvent F is added 0.01 mole of solute G, the freezing point of the solution is observed to be 0.56°C below the normal freezing point of the pure solvent F. The freezing-point-depression constant of material F is 7.0°C. What is the molecular weight of F?

9. A very dilute solution of sugar in water freezes at −0.0093°C (molal freezing-point-depression constant for water is 1.86). Instead of using R, use the molar-volume figure 22.4 liters STP in calculating the osmotic pressure that would be exerted by this solution at 0°C.

10. An aqueous solution containing 1% by weight of gum arabic—empirical formula $C_{12}H_{22}O_{11}$—was found to have an osmotic pressure of 7.2 mm of mercury at 0°C. The solution has a density very close to that of pure water.
(a) What is the apparent molecular weight of gum arabic?
(b) Assuming that for gum arabic the variation of the π/w ratio with concentration is of the same order as that shown in Fig. 4–15 for hemoglobin, what will be the percent error in the figure calculated in part (a)?

CONFIRMATIONS, EXTENSIONS, AND QUALIFICATIONS

In this last chapter we propose to consolidate the position attained in the first four—by confirming, extending, and qualifying some of the results obtained. What points should we consider?

By way of *confirmations*, observe that the whole elaborate structure built up in the last two chapters is founded, ultimately, on Cannizzaro's method for establishing the atomic weights of elements that form many volatile compounds. For the atomic weights so established were used in our development of Dulong and Petit's law—with which we went on then to assign atomic weights to the vast majority of (metallic) elements. All these atomic weights were then taken for granted as we pushed on to develop the laws of colligative phenomena, which permit us to assign molecular formulas to many compounds insusceptible to vapor-density studies. On what points in this development may we feel reservations? Cannizzaro's method is the keystone of our structure; but recall that the assignment of atomic weights by this method depends essentially on some assumption (e.g. an odd-number assumption, see p. 83) which, though eminently plausible, has not been *demonstrated* correct. Moreover, we are apt to retain some doubts about the validity of atomic weights assigned with the aid of the Dulong-and-Petit law, which may seem too approximate to deserve our complete confidence. Finally, we may remain skeptical of the great extrapolation involved when we apply, to molecules of immense molecular weight, an osmotic-pressure law that has been shown to be good only as a limiting law, and that can be tested only in its application to materials having much lower molecular weights assignable by other methods.

Thus what we must seek are:

(i) An independent way of establishing atomic weights, capable of confirming or challenging the assignments we have based on Cannizzaro's method and the Dulong-Petit law.

(ii) An independent method for establishing the molecular weights of the giant molecules so interesting to biochemists.

By way of *extensions*, note that while we have been able to assign *relative* atomic weights, we have as yet no basis for determining the *absolute* magnitudes to which they correspond. Though we need not know these magnitudes to handle the problems of classical chemistry, yet such magnitudes are data of obvious intrinsic interest—and also of very great relevance to many problems of *non*classical chemistry. Much the same statements may be made with regard to "Avogadro's number." We have been able to get along quite well without assigning any absolute value to it. But, again, that value is of intrinsic interest and, if available, would permit us to establish an absolute scale of atomic and molecular magnitudes. Consider also a second point. Though we have succeeded in developing methods competent to establish the molecular constitution of substances in the gaseous state and in the dissolved (liquid) state, we have so far touched on no method capable of establishing the constitution of substances in the solid state. That a given substance has the *same* molecular constitution, whether it is in the solid state or (say) vaporous, is certainly not an implausible assumption—but this is *only* an assumption. The foregoing considerations suggest that we must seek:

(i) Means for establishing the numerical value of Avogadro's number and, thence, the absolute scale of atomic and molecular magnitudes.

(ii) A method competent to shed light on the constitution of substances in the solid state.

By way of *qualifications*, we will find that—in the course of obtaining the above-indicated confirmations and extensions—we encounter certain new indications that demand some fundamental qualifications of the atomic and kinetic-molecular theories in the forms given them in earlier chapters. These qualifications we note as the need for them arises. But actually the need for some important (though *non*fundamental) qualifications of what has earlier been said will already have arisen—even as we carry through the inquiries described. We have said nothing whatever of the considerable number of outstanding "discrepancies," or cases of abnormal behavior, that our experiments will inevitably encounter. This policy is justifiable insofar as it helps us more readily grasp the broad regularities displayed in phenomena. But ultimately we must duly recognize, and cope with, the aberrant cases. Fortunately, all the discrepancies we have passed over in silence can be readily interpreted in terms of one general type of complication. We can then conveniently collect them together in a single group and discuss them *as* a group—as we do now.

Phenomena of Association and Dissociation

A vapor-density study of the element sulfur, made at temperatures just above its boiling point (445°C), yields data at least roughly consistent with an assignment of the molecular formula S_8 to sulfur in the vapor state. However, when vapor densities are measured at ca. 1200°C, the data obtained require an assignment of the molecular formula S_2 to sulfur in the vapor state. We cannot dismiss this discrepancy by making appeal to the known approximateness of the ideal gas laws as applied to real gases: the discrepancy is far too great thus to be dismissed. Must we then feel dismay at having found two irreconcilable formulas for sulfur in the vapor state? Not at all! Our two formulas do *not* refer to sulfur in the *same* state: the formula S_8 refers to sulfur vapor at 445°C, the formula S_2 to sulfur vapor at 1200°C. In all our earlier work we spoke of *stable* molecules and—*within the range of that stability*—a substance must, by definition, retain the same molecular constitution at different temperatures. On the other hand, we ought surely not to be dismayed if, *outside* the range of stability of one type of molecule, some other molecule is formed—with consequent change in the apparent molecular weight. In the case of sulfur, the S_8 molecule stable at 445° is unstable at 1200°C, and at the higher temperature it is the S_2 molecule that is stable.

When any such discrepancy is first encountered, one has the choice of imputing special behavior to the material at issue, as we have done above, or of supposing that the law engendering the discrepancy is somehow at fault. Thus, if the vapor density–molecular weight relation is supposed invalid at either the higher or lower temperature, we could entirely abolish the discrepancy that led us to impute special behavior to vaporous sulfur. But this supposition is quite unacceptable: we would have to challenge not only the vapor-density relation but also many gas laws well established in countless other applications. Amontons' law, for example, demands that —if we maintain constant volume and constant *quantity* of gas—the values of P and T measured at different temperatures must satisfy the relation $P/T = $ const. But if we heat a fixed weight of sulfur, in a fixed volume, from 445° to 1200°C, we find that the P/T quotient at the higher temperature is roughly four times that at the lower temperature. Again the discrepancy is far too large to dismiss as a reflection of the nonideality of real gases. But it is of course a discrepancy readily explicable on the supposition that the stable species in sulfur vapor at 445° is S_8 and at 1200°C is S_2.

For on this supposition it becomes clear that although we maintained constancy of the *weight* of sulfur, we did *not* maintain constancy of the number of *moles* of sulfur present. Though the weight is constant, the number of moles of gaseous particles of sulfur at 1200°C is four times the corresponding number at 445°C. And then, *naturally*, the P/T quotient is quadrupled between 445° and 1200°C.

In preference to crediting a *general* breakdown of the gas laws, which would be theoretically inexplicable, we understandably prefer to assume a special (but perfectly intelligible) behavior on the part of elemental sulfur. We need not doubt the gas laws, but we do recognize the need for some discrimination in interpreting the results they give for materials that, like sulfur, may exist in different molecular states under different conditions. Indeed the behavior of sulfur is not an isolated case. Of a great many other such cases, similarly explicable, we note but two. Consider the substance variously called nitrogen dioxide and nitrogen tetroxide. If we measure the vapor density of this substance at 0°C (and at low pressure, necessarily, since the boiling point is 21.3°C), our data imply a molecular weight of ca. 92, corresponding to the formula N_2O_4. But if we measure the vapor density at 140°C, our data imply a molecular weight of ca. 46, corresponding to the formula NO_2. Once again, the results are not fundamentally inconsistent: they signify only that the molecular species stable at 0° is not the molecular species stable at 140°C. Moreover, it is easy to show (as might also have been shown in the case of sulfur) the continuity of the transition from the low-temperature state, in which N_2O_4 is the predominant species, to the high-temperature state, in which NO_2 is predominant. "Molecular weights" determined at intermediate temperatures range continuously from one extreme to the other. Such "molecular weights" represent no more than *weighted averages*, reflecting the presence of *two* molecular species that occur in different proportions at different temperatures. And the consequent change in the total number of *moles* of gas, per *unit weight* of gas present, produces a continuously changing value of the Amontons P/T quotient—just as we found in the case of sulfur. Once again we will prefer to maintain the gas laws intact and to impute to our compound a molecular lability we can variously describe as the *association* of NO_2 to form N_2O_4 (at low temperatures) or as the *dissociation* of N_2O_4 to form NO_2 (at high temperatures). And in this case we can cite overwhelming independent evidence supporting this preference. Although at 0°C the nitrogen oxide is very nearly colorless, it becomes progressively darker-hued as the temperature rises and intensely reddish-brown by the time 140°C is reached. Surely this striking change in color is compelling evidence for belief that the substance undergoes *some* change between 0° and 140°C. And when we find that the continuous increase of color intensity with rising temperature precisely matches a corresponding continuous decline of apparent molecular weight with rising temperature, we surely have ample reason for concluding that "some change" is the progressive conversion of N_2O_4 (colorless) to NO_2 (red-brown).

One last example. If we measure the vapor density of phosphorus pentachloride at 150°C, the observed vapor density implies the molecular formula PCl_5. If we again measure the vapor density at ca. 300°C, we find it only half as great as we expect—apparently demanding the absurd formula $(PCl_5)_{1/2}$. Yet this result, and the corresponding discrepancies observed when the gas laws are applied to this system, are all satisfactorily explained if we suppose that the PCl_5 molecule stable at 150° has, by 300°C, become completely unstable with respect to the reaction $PCl_5 \rightarrow PCl_3 + Cl_2$. Thus *two* moles of gas (an equimolar mixture of PCl_3 and Cl_2) will be formed at high temperature from each mole of PCl_5 put in—with the effect that the vapor density is cut to half the value one would predict on the basis of the formula PCl_5. This decomposition reaction is then not fundamentally different from the examples of association-dissociation phenomena previously cited. And all such instances strongly underline the need for caution in the interpretation of vapor-density data that may, on occasion, refer not to a single stable molecular species but, rather, to variable mixtures of two or more species. Beyond this, however, these effects pose no real difficulty for (and demand no real revision or qualification of) the methods earlier developed only in terms of the "normal" behavior of stable molecules.

Turning now from vapors to solutions, we find similar discrepancies, similarly explicable as phenomena of association or dissociation. If, for example, we apply the method of freezing-point depression to the substance butyric acid dissolved in water, our data point to a solute molecular weight of the order of 88—consistent with the formula $C_4H_8O_2$ for butyric acid. But if, instead, we investigate solutions of butyric acid in another solvent (e.g. benzene), the data point to a molecular weight approximating 176—consistent with the formula $C_8H_{16}O_4$ for butyric acid. Two different molecular formulas for the *same substance* look grim. However observe that we are concerned with the "same substance" in quite different states—in water solution in one case, in benzene solution in the other. Such a change in solvent may well have effects every bit as drastic as the effects of a change of temperature on the molecular state of N_2O_4, etc. In fact, the butyric-acid case is readily explicable in the same terms: it is an association-dissociation phenomenon. And actually the phenomenon is a general one for many carboxylic acids—showing up not only in studies of *solutions* of these acids but also in vapor-density studies of the *pure* acids. At low temperatures the molecular weights indicated by such vapor-density studies are roughly twice as great as the molecular weights suggested by high-temperature data for the same substances, and the low and high values are entirely consistent with the corresponding low and high values found in studies of solutions of these acids.

An even more striking case is that of hydrogen chloride. Vapor-density data for pure hydrogen chloride yield molecular weights in the vicinity of 36, nicely consistent with the formula HCl. Freezing-point-depression data for dilute solutions of hydrogen chloride in such solvents as benzene yield roughly the same molecular weight and are thus also consistent with the formula HCl. But freezing-point-depression data for dilute *aqueous* solutions of hydrogen chloride imply a radically different situation. These data suggest a "molecular weight" approximating 18 and seem to demand the impossible formula $(HCl)_{1/2}$. Just such a case we have already encountered in the vapor-density study of PCl_5. When *one* mole of PCl_5 falls apart to yield *two* moles of a mixture of PCl_3 and Cl_2, the vapor-density data duly reflect the *average* molecular weight of the mixture. If then we insist on making a calculation in terms of a PCl_5 molecule that is totally or almost totally absent from the system, *of course* we find the absurd formula $(PCl_5)_{1/2}$. (Why?) In the same fashion, the formula $(HCl)_{1/2}$ indicated for hydrogen chloride, in aqueous solution, actually signifies that each HCl molecule has dissociated into two fragments. A truly immense body of independent evidence confirms this dissociation and permits us to identify the fragments.

Long before colligative properties were much studied, it was known that, unlike pure water, an aqueous solution of hydrogen chloride is a good conductor of electricity. That is, in aqueous solution (but not in benzene solution) hydrogen chloride is a "strong electrolyte." Moreover, when an electric current is thus passed through an aqueous solution of hydrogen chloride, gaseous hydrogen is liberated at the negative electrode and gaseous chlorine at the positive electrode. These data are most readily explained if we suppose that in aqueous solution an electrically neutral hydrogen-chloride molecule dissociates to give mobile charged particles capable of carrying a current; and the nature of the products obtained by electrolysis strongly suggests that the current-carrying particles are H^+ and Cl^- (or hydrated forms of these species). For a great many years it remained gravely in doubt whether these *ions* exist at all times in aqueous solutions of hydrogen chloride or, instead, are formed only at the instant one applies to the solution the potential difference required to make their presence manifest in conductivity and/or electrolytic effects. The colligative data banish all such doubts: in aqueous solution hydrogen chloride is apparently dissociated even when *no* potential difference is applied to the solution.

The phenomenon of ionization is a very general one. Dilute aqueous solutions of sodium chloride yield results similar to those obtained with hydrogen chloride. And we reject the repugnant formula $(NaCl)_{1/2}$ apparently implied, in favor of the concept of a dissociation forming Na^+ and Cl^- ions. With dilute aqueous barium chloride we obtain the absurd "molecular formula" $(BaCl_2)_{1/3}$ and promptly reject it in favor of the supposition that each $BaCl_2$ formula unit in the solution is present not as such but as $Ba^{++} + 2Cl^-$ ions. In these cases it is not merely naïve but impossible to interpret colligative-property data in terms of molecular formulas. As with the interpretation of vapor-density data for such materials as S_8, N_2O_4, and PCl_5, we must use discrimination in interpreting colligative-property data for solutes that can undergo dissociation. Actually the risk of misinterpretation is rather less in the second case, for we can always bring to bear an entirely independent method for detecting such dissociation. If a solution proves to be a good conductor of electricity, we are forewarned that colligative data for this solution may yield entirely spurious "molecular formulas." On the other hand, if a solution proves to be a *non*conductor of electricity, we may be sure at least that the complicating phenomenon of ionization is absent. Fortunately, the vast bulk of the organic substances to which we must assign molecular formulas on the basis of colligative data prove to be nonelectrolytes—particularly if we study them in nonionizing solvents like benzene—and for these substances our assignments of molecular formulas remain perfectly valid.

Nature often proves more complex than is at first supposed by mortals seeking to comprehend her. Phenomena of association and dissociation represent such an element of complexity. But the occurrence of such phenomena demands *no* fundamental revision of the structure of evidence and inference developed in earlier chapters. Some such revision is, however, required by the results of the inquiry to which we now turn.

X-ray Crystallography

The first quarter of the 20th century saw the development of a technique that, in its refined modern forms, permits us to map the structures of solids in precise detail at the atomic level. We shall entirely pass over the principles of this technique* and shall consider only a few of the general conclusions drawn from the results it makes accessible. These conclusions arise from data, and interpretative methods, wholly different from those we have discussed. Yet when, for example, an organic compound is mapped at the atomic level, we generally find that its crystal *does* contain distinguishable groups of atoms that exactly match, in number and identity, the molecular formula assigned by the methods developed in earlier chapters. This agreement is all the more delightful in that those methods permit the assignment of molecular formulas only to substances in a state of vaporization or solution. Given the broad range of variations opened up by the possible occurrence of association-dissociation phe-

---

* See W. H. Bragg and W. L. Bragg, *X-Rays and Crystal Structure*, G. Bell and Sons, 1924.

nomena, it is a potentially hazardous extrapolation to assign to a substance in its solid state the molecular formula we have obtained by working with it as a vapor or in solution. When x-ray crystallographic data open to us, for the first time, a view of the solid state, we do indeed encounter some cases in which that extrapolation fails (and for reasons we now feel we understand). But, in the vast majority of cases, the x-ray data do most satisfactorily confirm the molecular formulas assigned to organic compounds by the classical methods of chemistry.

What of such substances as sodium chloride? Here the x-ray data reveal a surprising vista. A crystal of sodium chloride appears to consist of a perfectly uniform lattice-work of alternating sodium and chlorine atoms we can visualize as built up from identical "unit cells" like that shown in Fig. 5–1, merging each into the next, and continuing without a break throughout the extent of the crystal. Actually, the lattice units are better described not as atoms but as sodium and chloride *ions*. Thus we learn that the Na^+ and Cl^- ions, indicated as present in aqueous solutions of sodium chloride, are *not* freshly formed by dissociation as that substance dissolves but, rather, pre-exist as such in crystalline sodium chloride. Equally surprising, and more immediately relevant, is one further conclusion drawn from the x-ray data. In the crystal, each sodium stands equidistant from a number of chlorines, each chlorine stands equidistant from a number of sodiums, and there are absolutely *no* localized groupings that can be thought to represent a sodium chloride *molecule*. As applied to such a structure, the whole idea of a molecular formula is simply *meaningless*.

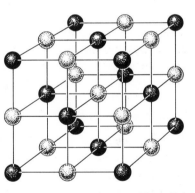

Figure 5–1

How do these findings relate to the position we earlier developed? Observe that we have *never* had occasion to discuss a molecular-weight method applicable to substances *in the solid state*. The methods we applied to the study of solutions and vapors remain completely unimpugned by the discovery that, in some cases, molecular groupings simply do not exist in the solid state. To be sure, we did devote a good deal of attention to the Dulong-and-Petit law. But observe that from this law we obtained *only empirical formulas* and, even for an ionic compound like sodium chloride, the concept of empirical formula remains entirely meaningful. That is, x-ray crystallography *does* show that in sodium chloride, the atoms or ions of sodium and chlorine are combined in a 1:1 proportion. And in general, the x-ray data provide remarkably satisfactory confirmations of all the empirical formulas we assigned to solids by using the Dulong-and-Petit law. In all of this there is no occasion for dismay, but only for rejoicing.

The x-ray data do, however, suggest the need for one significant qualification of the third postulate we used in framing our atomic theory (see p. 5): "A chemical compound consists of molecules . . ." This statement offered us a simple approach to the problems we faced at that time, but it is now recognizable as an oversimplification easily avoided in some such statement as the following.

> When a chemical compound is formed from the elements, the numbers of atoms of the elements entering into combination stand to each other* in the ratio of definite, small, integral numbers.

In effect, this rather more elaborate statement entails the existence *only* of empirical formulas—but without at all excluding the possible existence of molecular formulas. Quite sufficient to have supported our early development of the atomic theory, this restatement of the third postulate remains completely unshaken by our present discovery that to some compounds the concept of molecular formula is not meaningfully applicable.

When we deal with definite molecular groupings, the gain or loss of a single atom must produce a radically different molecule having its own distinctive properties, i.e. a molecule of a *different compound*, as CO_2 differs from CO. But when we deal with an extended lattice array containing *no* molecular groupings, we readily grasp the possibility of a totally new situation. Suppose that a *few* atoms of one or the other element are missing from some of the lattice sites, or that a *few* additional atoms of one or the other element are fitted in between the normal lattice sites. Given the enormous *total* number of atoms present in the crystal as a whole, its observable macroscopic chemical properties may still remain substantially unchanged. What is chemically "the same compound" might, in this case, show a slight variability in composition (depending on the method used in preparing it) in defiance of the law of definite proportions. Refined methods of chemical analysis actually *do* detect such a variability in certain nonmolecular compounds. Ordinarily the range of variation is miniscule, and we render adequate account of it when we insert the words "very nearly" in our restatement of the third postulate of our atomic theory. However, with such materials as ZnO, FeS, and many other metallic sulfides and oxides, the range of variability may be considerably extended. In a few instances, that range is so broadened that it covers the entire span between two different classical formulas: in the change from Ce_2S_3 to Ce_3S_4 for

---

* For reasons that will soon be apparent, we should insert here the words "very nearly."

example, a continuous series of intermediate compositions links the two extremes represented by the formulas. Such materials have no bearing whatever on the law of definite proportions: they are *not* compounds. Although such a material is sometimes referred to as a "nonstoichiometric compound," it is far better denoted by the neutral word "phase." In effect, it may be regarded as a solid solution: like all known solutions, it is clearly a mixture variable in its proportions and completely homogeneous at the macroscopic level because it contains no distinct particles larger than atomic-molecular dimensions. These nonstoichiometric materials are obviously ill-suited for, and to be avoided in, stoichiometric studies of the sort we have used to implement our atomic theory. But beyond this word of caution we need not go. There is *nothing* about such materials that is in principle inexplicable in atomistic terms and, consequently, the occurrence of such materials demands no fundamental revision of the conceptual structure we have built up.

As a more than adequate compensation for the slight check recognized in the last paragraph, results readily obtained from x-ray crystallography permit us to push our atomic theory forward to the point of assigning absolute values to atomic magnitudes. This possibility arises because, with those results in hand, we can easily proceed to a determination of Avogadro's number, N. Consider that x-ray crystallography reveals not only the make-up of the unit cell but also its dimensions. In the case of sodium chloride for example, the unit cell shown in the preceding figure is a cube 5.6392×10^{-8} cm to an edge. Our previous studies of relative atomic weights allow us to assign 58.456 as the relative formula weight of NaCl, and a determination of the density of crystalline sodium chloride yields the figure 2.1642 gm/cm^3. The last two figures, together, permit a calculation of the total volume occupied by one gram-formula of crystalline NaCl:

$$\text{molar volume of NaCl} = \frac{58.456}{2.1642} = 27.009 \text{ cm}^3.$$

The cube root of 27.009 is excellently approximated as 3.000, whence it follows that one gram formula of crystalline NaCl will occupy a cubic block with edge length of 3.000 cm. Let us now imagine this macroscopic cube as built up from an entirely regular array of cubic unit cells that fill it completely. Along any edge of the macroscopic cube, the distance between adjacent atoms is 2.8196×10^{-8} cm ($=5.6392 \times 10^{-8}/2$ cm). Hence the total number of atoms lying along any edge of the macroscopic cube is

$$\frac{3.000}{2.820} \times 10^8.$$

Atoms appear with the same spacing throughout the macroscopic cube.

Confirmations, Extensions, and Qualifications

Hence we can easily establish the total number of atoms (or ions) present therein:

$$\text{total number of atoms} = \left[\frac{3.000}{2.820} \times 10^8\right]^3 = 1.205 \times 10^{24}.$$

Sodiums make up half this total, chlorines the other half; and for the number of NaCl formula units present in one gram-formula weight of NaCl we write

$$\text{total number of formula units} = \frac{1.205}{2} \times 10^{24} = 6.02 \times 10^{23}.$$

This figure represents also the number of sodium atoms in one gram-atom of sodium, the number of chlorine atoms in one gram-atom of chlorine, the number of carbon atoms in one gram-atom of carbon, the number of gaseous particles in 22.4 liter STP of an ideal gas, etc. In a word, it is Avogadro's number N. And given the almost unimaginable immensity of the number so compactly expressed as 6×10^{23}, we grasp the almost unimaginable minuteness of atomic magnitudes—all of which can now easily be evaluated. For example, 1.0 gm of hydrogen is also the gram-atomic mass containing as many atoms of hydrogen as there are atoms of carbon in 12.0 gm of carbon. Hence

$$\text{mass of one hydrogen atom} = \frac{1}{6.02 \times 10^{23}} = 1.66 \times 10^{-24}\text{gm}.$$

Carbon, with a relative atomic weight of 12, will then have an absolute mass 12 times that of hydrogen, 1.99×10^{-23} gm, and so on for other species.

The Barometric Formula and Boltzmann's Distribution Law

We here begin a substantial digression to consider a specific problem which, of some interest in itself, will also point toward a profoundly important relation having more than a little bearing on our study. The specific problem is: How does pressure vary with altitude in "the sea of the air" (Torricelli's phrase) at the bottom of which we dwell? Contenting ourselves with an approximate answer, we can avoid the great complexities of this problem by making several drastic simplifying assumptions. We will find it easy enough to get an answer if we assume that we have to deal only with an *isothermal* atmosphere made up of a *single ideal gas* with molecular weight ca. 29 ($\doteq \frac{1}{5}M_{\text{oxy}} + \frac{4}{5}M_{\text{nit}} = \frac{1}{5}\,32 + \frac{4}{5}\,28 = 6.4 + 22.4 = 28.8$).

Consider first the phenomenon of pressure as it manifests itself at the bottom of a column of *liquid* with density ρ. The density represents the mass of a unit volume (say 1 cm^3) of liquid, and at the surface of the earth the gravitational force exerted on this mass is just ρg, where g is the gravitational acceleration ($=980$ cm/sec^2). If we consider a deep column of liquid—1 cm^2 in cross section and h_0 cm deep—the total volume of liquid present is h_0 cm^3, the total mass of liquid is $h_0\rho$, the total gravitational force exerted on the contents of the column is $h_0\rho g$, and the hydrostatic pressure exerted on the 1-cm^2 surface supporting the bottom of the column must then also be $h_0\rho g$. If we assign a *negative* sign to distance measured *down from the top* surface of the liquid, the positive value of the pressure at *any* depth (h) in the liquid will then be given as

$$P = -\rho g h.$$

To assume that g is constant, throughout even a column many miles in extent, is quite permissible. The value of g depends on the inverse square of distance measured *not* from the surface of the earth but, rather, from the *center* thereof. At the surface of the earth this distance is already some 4000 miles, and an increase (or decrease) of a good many miles can then be made without significant change in the value of g. Actually, the above formula is far less vulnerable on the score of a possible variation in g than it is in regard to a possible variation of ρ. Liquids are not easily compressed, but they are far from being incompressible. To the extent that they *are* compressible, the density at the bottom of a column of liquid even one mile deep may be quite appreciably different from the density at the top. A liquid like water is sufficiently incompressible to make the above equation a reasonable approximation for columns of considerable depth. But that equation will be inadmissable even as an approximation when we come, as we now do, to consider the pressure at the bottom of a column of ideal gas—whose ready compressibility is expressed in Boyle's law.

Having developed a formula at least approximately applicable to determination of the variation of pressure with *depth* (measured *down from the surface*) in a sea of water, let us turn now to the variation of pressure with *altitude* (measured *up from the bottom*) in a sea of air. Symbolizing by Δh the *positive* value of a short distance measured upward, we symbolize by ΔP the *negative* change of pressure encountered as one proceeds upward a distance Δh. But now consider this ugly problem: How shall we represent the density of air (δ) prevailing over this distance? From the ideal-gas law, we earlier derived (p. 68) the equation now rewritten as

$$\delta = PM/RT.$$

This equation makes it painfully evident that as the pressure varies over the distance Δh, so too must the density of air. Rather than capitulate in the face of this difficulty, let us assume provisionally that, over a *very short distance* Δh, the density varies so little that it can be approximated by some *one* value, δ. For a very short column of air we may, then, write an equation much like that earlier written for more extended columns of liquid:

$$\Delta P = -\delta g \, \Delta h.$$

Starting with the known pressure (P_0) of air at the surface of the earth $(h_0 \equiv 0)$, we seek now to calculate the pressure (P_1) at the altitude (h_1) attained by making a very small upward step Δh. Assuming the density constant at its *initial* value (δ_0), we can establish P_1 by considering the pressure decrement (ΔP_1) consequent to this ascent:

$$\Delta P_1 = P_1 - P_0 = -\delta_0 g \, \Delta h,$$

$$P_1 = P_0 - \delta_0 g \, \Delta h.$$

Expressing δ_0 in terms of P_0, we have then

$$P_1 = P_0 - \frac{P_0 M}{RT} g \, \Delta h,$$

or

$$P_1 = P_0 \left[1 - \frac{Mg}{RT} \Delta h \right].$$

To this pressure, at altitude h_1, corresponds a density (δ_1) given as

$$\delta_1 = \frac{P_1 M}{RT} = \frac{M}{RT} P_0 \left[1 - \frac{Mg}{RT} \Delta h \right] = \frac{P_0 M}{RT} \left[1 - \frac{Mg}{RT} \Delta h \right].$$

Now we are ready to take a *second* short upward step (Δh) to reach the total altitude h_2 at which the pressure is P_2. Approximating the density as constant at its initial value (δ_1) for *this* interval, we write

$$\Delta P_2 = P_2 - P_1 = -\delta_1 g \, \Delta h,$$

$$P_2 = P_1 - \delta_1 g \, \Delta h.$$

Substituting the expressions previously obtained for P_1 and δ_1, we find

$$P_2 = P_0 \left[1 - \frac{Mg}{RT} \Delta h \right] - \frac{P_0 M}{RT} \left[1 - \frac{Mg}{RT} \Delta h \right] g \, \Delta h$$

$$= P_0 \left[1 - \frac{Mg}{RT} \Delta h \right] \left[1 - \frac{Mg}{RT} \Delta h \right] = P_0 \left[1 - \frac{Mg}{RT} \Delta h \right]^2.$$

The density (δ_2) at altitude h_2 is now calculable in terms of P_0, and we can then proceed to a *third* step Δh. The situation is strongly reminiscent of familiar compound-interest calculations. And it is easy to see that when we have made n incremental ascents Δh, to reach the total altitude h_n, the pressure (P_n) prevailing there will be simply

$$P_n = P_0 \left[1 - \frac{Mg}{RT} \Delta h \right]^n.$$

This is a *general* expression, potentially applicable at all altitudes. But, except in the limiting case we must now examine, it is only *approximate*. Knowing that over any finite distance the density *must* change in response to the change of pressure we seek to calculate, we nevertheless applied, *throughout* each step of distance Δh, the density at the bottom of this step. Our representation of a changing density by a constant density is an approximation that becomes better the smaller the height increment Δh involved, but this representation remains *only* an approximation save in the limit of $\Delta h \to 0$. But, with $\Delta h \to 0$, a finite altitude can be attained only as $n \to \infty$, and it remains to be seen how we can handle the above equation in these apparently difficult circumstances.

Consider *any* two altitudes (h_j and h_i, with $h_j > h_i$) at which reign any two pressures (P_j and P_i, with $P_j < P_i$). If, in proceeding from h_i to h_j, we take s equal steps, the upward distance (Δh) in each such step must be

$$\Delta h = \frac{h_j - h_i}{s}.$$

We can then express the relation of P_j to P_i by the equation

$$P_j = P_i \left[1 - \frac{Mg}{RT} \left(\frac{h_j - h_i}{s} \right) \right]^s.$$

This relation should be rigorous in the limit (and *only* in the limit) of $\Delta h \to 0$. That is to say, if $h_j - h_i$ is finite, in the limit $s \to \infty$. What form will the equation assume as $s \to \infty$? A trivial change of variable makes it unexpectedly easy to answer this question. We define

$$\alpha = - \frac{sRT}{Mg(h_j - h_i)}$$

and substitute to obtain

$$P_j = P_i \left\{ 1 + \frac{1}{\alpha} \right\}^{-\alpha Mg(h_j - h_i)/RT}$$

or

$$P_j = P_i \left[\left\{ 1 + \frac{1}{\alpha} \right\}^\alpha \right]^{-Mg(h_j - h_i)/RT}.$$

From the definition of α it follows that in the limit $s \to \infty$ so also does $\alpha \to \infty$. We have then only to establish the value of the function $(1 + 1/\alpha)^\alpha$ in the limit $\alpha \to \infty$. With a log table, we can easily evaluate

TABLE 5–1

α	1	2	10	100	1000	10,000
$\left(1+\dfrac{1}{\alpha}\right)^{\alpha}$	2.000	2.250	2.594	2.705	2.718	2.718

the function at various increasing finite values of α. Table 5–1 displays the results so obtained: the function converges slowly but perfectly smoothly toward a limiting value, which proves to be 2.71828 . . . Possessed of quite remarkable mathematical properties, this incommensurable number is conventionally assigned the symbol e—in terms of which we can readily give compact expression to our last equation:

$$P_j/P_i = e^{-Mg(h_j-h_i)/RT}$$

This is the so-called barometric formula (historically associated with the name of Laplace) which makes it easy to determine a difference of two altitudes from the observable ratio of barometric readings made at these altitudes.*

Parenthetically, it is worth while to note the frequent occurrence in science of equations similar in form to the barometric formula. In the decay of some one radioactive species, for example, the number of atoms (n_1) present at a time t_1 is related to the number (n_2) present at some other time t_2 by the equation:

$$\frac{n_2}{n_1} = e^{-L(t_2-t_1)},$$

where L is a constant characteristic of the species concerned. Similarly, when light is passed through a colored solution, the intensity of the light (I_1) at a depth l_1 in the solution is related to its intensity (I_2) at some other depth l_2 by the equation

$$\frac{I_2}{I_1} = e^{-K(l_2-l_1)},$$

---

* For purposes of calculation, it is most convenient to recast the equation by taking the denary logarithms of both sides:

$$\log \frac{P_j}{P_i} = \log e^{-Mg(h_j-h_i)/RT} = \frac{-Mg(h_j - h_i)}{RT} \log e$$

$$= \frac{-Mg(h_j - h_i)}{RT} \log 2.718 = \frac{-Mg(h_j - h_i)}{RT} (0.4343),$$

or

$$\log \frac{P_j}{P_i} = \frac{-Mg}{2.303\,RT} (h_j - h_i).$$

where K is a constant dependent on the nature and concentration of the absorbing material and on the wavelength of the light involved. Equations of this form are *always* obtained when, at any point, the rate of decline of some parameter (e.g. pressure, number of radioactive atoms, intensity of light) is directly proportional to the value of the parameter at that point. Thus the rate of pressure decline at any altitude is directly proportional to the density at that altitude and—density being directly proportional to pressure—also to the pressure at that altitude. All such equations are conspicuously easy to derive. Indeed, the student who knows some calculus will, no doubt, long since have recognized the possibility of a more expeditious derivation of the barometric formula—proceeding directly from the first equation on p. 148. That equation, $\Delta P = -\delta g\,\Delta h$, can be rewritten:

$$dP = -\delta g\,dh = -\frac{PM}{RT}\,g\,dh,$$

$$d\ln P = -\frac{Mg}{RT}\,dh.$$

Integration of this differential equation at once yields the barometric formula with which we ended the preceding paragraph.

However he derives it, the student may still be disposed to ask: "What do we want with a barometric formula anyhow?" Among other things, surprisingly enough, it yields (as shown in Appendix II) a straightforward and rigorous derivation of the osmotic-pressure law used *without* derivation in the last chapter. Even more important, consideration of the barometric formula will carry us on toward an enormously significant abstract relation, of which that formula is but one concrete expression. We have only a little way to go. Imagine an isothermal ideal gas present in a tall column of uniform cross section. Within this column, let us consider an infinitesimally thin slice of volume V^* at the altitude h_j, and another such slice of identical volume at the altitude h_i. We ask now for the ratio of the number (η_j) of molecules present in the slice at height h_j to the number (η_i) of molecules present in the slice at h_i (Fig. 5–2). The *moles* of gas present in each slice can be expressed as η_j/N and η_i/N, where N is Avogadro's number, and the ideal-gas law then permits us to write

$$P_jV^* = \frac{\eta_j}{N}RT \quad \text{and} \quad P_iV^* = \frac{\eta_i}{N}RT.$$

Recalling that the gas is stipulated isothermal, we can at once draw from these equations a relation probably obvious enough even without derivation:

$$P_j/P_i = \eta_j/\eta_i.$$

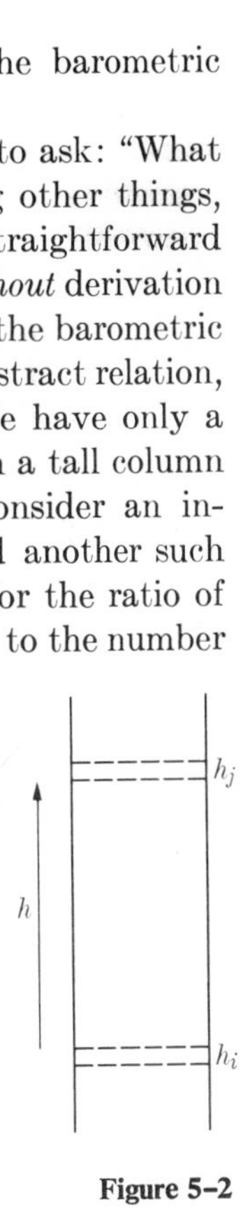

Figure 5–2

Substituting now in the last expression of the barometric formula, we find

$$\eta_j/\eta_i = e^{-Mg(h_j-h_i)/RT},$$

which offers the sought-for ratio of the numbers of particles present in equal volumes at different altitudes.

Let us now examine more attentively the right-hand side of the last equation. The symbol M represents the gram-molecular weight of the gas in question and, if we perform the division M/N, the quotient is the mass (m) of a single gas particle. Similarly, if we divide R by N, we obtain the universal constant k—for remember that R was originally defined as $R = Nk$. Consequently

$$\frac{Mg}{RT} = \frac{(M/N)g}{(R/N)T} = \frac{mg}{kT},$$

which, on substitution in our last equation, yields

$$\eta_j/\eta_i = e^{-mg(h_j-h_i)/kT}.$$

The grouping $mg(h_j - h_i)$ can now be given a much more suggestive expression. The term mg represents the gravitational force acting on a single gas particle; $(h_j - h_i)$ is the distance between the two levels under consideration. Suppose that we were to transport a gas particle from level h_i to level h_j: we would have to do work = force × distance = $mg(h_j - h_i)$. This work input reflects the increment of gravitational potential energy acquired by the particle when it is transported from h_i to h_j—energy recovered again as work output if the particle is allowed to drop back from h_j to h_i. Thus the expression $mg(h_j - h_i)$ represents *the excess potential energy* possessed by a particle at height h_j as compared with the energy it would possess at height h_i. Symbolizing this (positive) excess as $\Delta\epsilon$, we can rewrite our last equation in the following compact form:

$$\eta_j/\eta_i = e^{-\Delta\epsilon/kT}.$$

In a column containing many gas particles—each of which may be found at *any* level—the ratio of the numbers present at any two levels can now be expressed as a function of the energy difference between these levels. Note that, having taken h_j above h_i, we should find $\eta_j < \eta_i$, or $\eta_j/\eta_i < 1$. This *is* just what our formula will yield: both k and T are positive numbers, as is also $\Delta\epsilon$ in this case. Consequently $\Delta\epsilon/kT$ is a *positive* number, and $e^{-\Delta/\epsilon kT}$ is then a number less than 1. That is

$$e^{-\Delta/\epsilon kT} = \frac{1}{e^{+\Delta\epsilon/kT}} < 1 \qquad \text{whenever } \Delta\epsilon > 0.$$

Beyond confirming our qualitative expectation that $\eta_j/\eta_i < 1$, the above formula supplies also a quantitative value for that ratio. Other things being equal, the greater the separation of the two levels the greater is the magnitude of $\Delta\epsilon$, and the greater the margin by which the ratio of particle numbers differs from 1. Conversely, for a given separation of level (i.e. fixed $\Delta\epsilon$), the margin by which the ratio of particle numbers differs from 1 will be smaller the higher the temperature (T).

The formula $\eta_j/\eta_i = e^{-\Delta\epsilon/kT}$ has been derived for a special kind of system of no very great theoretical interest. However, a far more subtle and abstract line of (statistical mechanical) reasoning yields exactly the same equation as an expression of the equilibrium distribution of a set of *any* weakly interacting particles that can occupy *any* set of energetic states —provided only that each state is potentially open, with equal *a priori* probability, to each of the particles present. That is, the above equation, for the distribution in height of an isothermal ideal gas, is but one specific expression of a *general* relation which is not merely the most important relation appearing in this book but one of the most important relations known to modern science. This is the Boltzmann distribution law:

$$\eta_j/\eta_i = e^{-\Delta\epsilon/kT} \quad .$$

Observe that neither $\Delta\epsilon$ nor kT singly is as significant as the *energy ratio* $\Delta\epsilon/kT$.* When this ratio is large (i.e. large $\Delta\epsilon$ and/or low temperature), the particle-number ratio is $\ll 1$; that is, the particles are very unevenly distributed between the two energetic states. When the ratio $\Delta\epsilon/kT$ is small (i.e. small $\Delta\epsilon$ and/or high temperature) the particle-number ratio approaches 1; that is, the particles become more evenly distributed over the two energetic states. As a useful standard of reference, note that for $\Delta\epsilon = kT$,

$$\eta_j/\eta_i = e^{-1} = 1/2.718 = 0.368.$$

We have *not* derived the Boltzmann law as the very general relation it is, but if we are prepared to credit its general validity, we can at once bring it to bear on at least three points highly relevant to the inquiry we have been pursuing.

Avogadro's number from studies of sedimentation equilibrium. Given the Boltzmann law, we can evaluate Avogadro's number (N) in another way. Actually, it was in this way that the *first* completely convincing determination of Avogadro's number was made, by Perrin, years before the development of x-ray crystallography opened the route already discussed. The

---

* Originally introduced (p. 46) as an expression of translational kinetic energy, kT must (like $\Delta\epsilon$) have the dimensions of energy per particle.

system studied by Perrin was a suspension of particles so minute that they display the so-called *Brownian motion*. A fascinating phenomenon in itself, this motion constitutes one of the singly most compelling items of evidence supporting the kinetic-molecular theory. On that theory we conceive the steady "pressure" exerted by a gas on the walls of its container as arising from discrete, abrupt processes: the collisions of gas particles with the walls. At any sizable surface the number of collisions in unit time is so enormous that the net force thus produced is apparently steady and free from detectable fluctuations. However, an entirely different situation may emerge when one is concerned with exceedingly minute particles—exposing only minute surfaces and having minute masses. In a fluid suspension of such particles, one might well hope to detect random fluctuations in the molecular bombardment to which each particle is subjected. If the collisions, with the minute surfaces exposed by each particle, are sufficiently small in number, there must occur appreciable momentary imbalances of the forces acting on opposite surfaces of the same particle. The imbalance of force may never be very large but, when the mass of the particle is minute enough, even a slight imbalance of force suffices to give that particle a detectable acceleration. The direction of the force-imbalance being subject to random fluctuation, the particle will thus be driven first in one direction, then in another.

Just such an erratic motion of microscopic particles was first observed, in an aqueous suspension of plant pollen, by the botanist Robert Brown in 1827. The cytoplasmic granules in this suspension are never at rest but are forever dancing in chaotic motion apparently completely independent from one particle to another—and, hence, *not* attributable to mass motion of the medium. At one time thought a *vital* phenomenon (i.e. a manifestation displayed only by materials of animal or vegetable origin) this motion remained a puzzle for some 50 years. Ultimately the kinetic argument outlined above showed that—far from being a puzzle—the Brownian motion is a consequence *entailed* by the application of the kinetic-molecular theory to particles of sufficient minuteness. Such particles are *exceedingly* minute, and a really vigorous Brownian motion is found only with particles so small that they can be seen with a microscope only as bright spots of diffuse scattered light. To this extent, however, *we can see* a particle which —though immense in comparison with true molecules—moves in response to molecular motions, with energies reflecting molecular kinetic energies. From a study of such particles we may, then, expect to gain some perspective on the scale of molecular magnitudes.

By grinding up *gamboge*,* a water-insoluble plant resin, one obtains minute particles of a bright yellow pigment used by artists. Subjecting a

---

* The name is a corruption of "Cambodia," whence gamboge was obtained.

suspension of such particles to repeated fractional centrifugation—in which larger particles settle more rapidly than smaller particles of the same substance—Perrin was able to obtain preparations containing many gamboge particles approximately equal in size (and approximately spherical in shape). The *size* of these particles could be determined as follows. By careful microscopic examination, counting the somewhat diffuse spots of scattered light, one can determine the number (α) of particles in a given suspension of gamboge in water. By evaporating the water, one can recover the gamboge particles and determine their *collective weight* (β) with a microbalance. The bulk density of gamboge (ρ_s) can, of course, easily be established; it approximates 1.2 gm/cm³. Assuming that one has substantially uniform and approximately spherical particles, with radius r, the volume of each particle is $\frac{4}{3}\pi r^3$. The *individual particle mass* (m_s) is then $\frac{4}{3}\pi r^3 \rho_s$, and the value of r is at once determinable from the following equation, in which it figures as the only unknown:

$$\tfrac{4}{3}\pi r^3 \rho_s \alpha = \beta.$$

For the particles used by Perrin in his studies, r is of the order of 10^{-4} mm.

Consider a short column of liquid containing a suspension of uniform gamboge particles—now of *known size*. Two opposing forces act upon these particles. One is the net force of gravity (corrected for buoyancy, *vide infra*), acting to collect the particles together at the bottom of the container. The other is the resultant of the random molecular bombardment producing the Brownian motion, and acts to keep the particles dispersed in the suspension. This opposition leads to the establishment of a *concentration gradient*: the particles are most numerous toward the bottom of the liquid column, least numerous toward its top, and the particle concentration falls off exponentially from the bottom to the top.* By actually counting the particles visible in the field of his microscope, Perrin was able to show that the number of particles/cm³ at a given level is only about $\frac{1}{2}$ the corresponding concentration of particles at a level some 0.05 mm lower.† Given this concentration gradient, and the previously established size of the individual gamboge particles, we can now bring the Boltzmann distribution law to bear on a calculation of Avogadro's number.

---

* This is exactly the kind of distribution we found for molecules in a tall isothermal column of air, where also the distribution reflects the opposition of a gravitational force and the kinetic energies of particle motions. However, while the air particles are invisible, the individual gamboge particles can be seen, counted, and (as above) assigned an *individual mass*.

† In a column of air, where the individual particles are *much* smaller, such a ratio of particle concentrations is found only at levels some 5 km apart.

Compare the gravitational potential energy of a gamboge particle at any two heights, h_i and h_j, in Perrin's suspension. The particle, with mass m_s, is drawn down by a gravitational force given as

$$F_{\text{down}} = m_s g = \tfrac{4}{3}\pi r^3 \rho_s g.$$

The particle is also buoyed up by a force that, from Archimedes principle, is equal to the weight of the liquid medium it displaces; this force is given as

$$F_{\text{up}} = m_1 g = \tfrac{4}{3}\pi r^3 \rho_1 g,$$

where m_1 and ρ_1, respectively, signify the mass and density of the displaced liquid. For the *net* force acting on the particles we have then

$$F_{\text{net}} = \tfrac{4}{3}\pi r^3 g(\rho_s - \rho_1).$$

Taking level h_j above level h_i, we see that the work invested in transporting the particle from h_i to h_j will represent the surplus potential energy $(\Delta\epsilon)$ possessed by that particle when it is at h_j rather than at h_i. Thus we write

$$\Delta\epsilon = \text{work} = \text{net force} \cdot \text{distance} = \tfrac{4}{3}\pi r^3 g(\rho_s - \rho_1)(h_j - h_i).$$

Applying Boltzmann's formula to the gamboge suspension, we obtain

$$\eta_j/\eta_i = e^{-4\pi r^3 g(\rho_s - \rho_1)(h_j - h_i)/3kT}.$$

We know the ratio η_j/η_i for some known distance $(h_j - h_i)$, we know r, and we know also g, ρ_s, ρ_1, and T. Thus the above equation may be solved for the Boltzmann constant, k. Now recall that R has been defined (see p. 62) as Nk and, from our studies of gases, we already possess a value of R. Hence, with the value of k just obtained, we can solve the equation $N = R/k$ for the value of Avogadro's number, N. The value so determined by Perrin was 6.5×10^{23}, which—considering the enormous difficulty of his mode of experimentation—is in excellent agreement with the modern figure 6.02×10^{23} obtained from x-ray crystallography and a great variety of other methods. Observe that in the Perrin determination, the Boltzmann law is deployed in a context rather different from that in which the barometric formula was developed as a special case. The success of Perrin's application thus represents a heartening indication that the Boltzmann law does "make sense" generally.

High molecular weights from studies of sedimentation equilibrium. As a second application of the Boltzmann law, consider how very nearly the same line of argument provides the basis for a method of determining molecular weights that fall within, *and beyond,* the range of those to which we have so far been able to apply only the osmotic-pressure method. In a vertical column of an isothermal solution containing large molecules, they distribute themselves in response to two opposed influences: the pull of gravity, which acts to collect them together, and the dispersive effect arising from the molecules' own kinetic energies. The relative concentrations at which the molecules establish themselves at different heights in the solution cannot, of course, be established by direct counting, since (unlike gamboge particles) the molecules are invisible. However, the relative concentrations can easily be determined spectrophotometrically —i.e. by measuring, at various heights in the column, the extent to which the solution passes a transverse beam of light having a wavelength known to be selectively absorbed by the molecular species in question. Can we not, then, at once proceed very much as Perrin did? No! Perrin's gamboge particles, though minute, are vastly larger than true molecules. That is, making due allowance for the buoyancy of the medium, the effective mass of a gamboge particle ($m_{\text{eff}} = \frac{4}{3}\pi r^3[\rho_s - \rho_1]$) vastly exceeds the corresponding effective mass of any true molecule (m_{eff}^*). To raise a gamboge particle over some vertical distance (Δh) as short as a few hundredths of a millimeter requires an energy ($\Delta\epsilon = m_{\text{eff}}g\,\Delta h$) which is large compared with kT—so that the particle-concentration gradient is very steep and readily measurable in even a shallow container. However, the transport of a true molecule over the same vertical distance will require an energy, $\Delta\epsilon^*$, that is vastly inferior to $\Delta\epsilon$ and—with $\Delta\epsilon^*$ actually much smaller than kT—the molecule-concentration gradient is far too slight to be detected in any column of solution short enough to be manageable experimentally. How then shall we proceed?

If we rely only on settling in the earth's gravitational field, we are at a dead end. But Svedberg bethought himself of the possibilities presented when sedimentation equilibrium is established in centrifugal fields. In his "ultracentrifuge," a centrifugal acceleration (g^*) of the order of 300,000 g can be reached and steadily maintained. The force promoting sedimentation is thus enormously increased and, compared to kT, the energy $\Delta\epsilon^*$ ($= m_{\text{eff}}^* g^* \Delta r$) becomes quite substantial over even very short distances (Δr) perpendicular to the axis of rotation of the centrifuge. By using the method of light absorption, one can determine the ratio of the equilibrium concentrations of the molecules at various distances from the axis of rotation—*while* the solution is being spun in the centrifuge. From these measurements, together with certain empirically determinable accessory data, one can establish the molecular weight of the dissolved substance by bringing the Boltzmann distribution law to bear. For an easy route to the requisite equation, see Problem 8 on p. 171. The results obtained by this method are in good (though by no means perfect) agreement with the results obtained for the same substances by the osmotic-pressure method earlier discussed. Even more important, the ultracentrifuge method can be extended into a region of molecular vastness inaccessible to even the most refined osmotic-pressure work—a region extending up to a value of some 30,000,000 for the "molecular weight" of tobacco mosaic virus.

The Maxwell-Boltzmann speed distribution. Instead of advancing our studies into new domains, as do the two points so far noted, a third point suggested by the Boltzmann distribution law demands rather that we qualify what was asserted of a domain long since left behind. The distribution of translational kinetic energies in a gas also conforms to the Boltzmann law. We cannot *derive*, nor will we even state, the rather complex function that describes this energy distribution. A sketch of the distribution of molecular speeds in a gas at two different temperatures is given in Fig. 5–3. Even at room temperature the spread of molecular speeds is not only quite broad but also notably asymmetric—due to the long "tail" that stretches out asymptotically toward high speeds. In our earlier derivation of the ideal gas laws, we blandly used a single velocity ($\overline{u}$) to represent the average velocity of all particles in a gas at a given temperature. In view of the broad and asymmetric spread of these velocities, it is not at all obvious that our earlier derivation was *at all* legitimate. However, either then or now, careful and complete derivations would involve us in very deep complexities. And, happily, such derivations support the same conclusions we obtained by "derivations" neither careful nor complete. Hence the fabric of reasoning we used to obtain atomic weights and molecular formulas needs *no* reweaving. In this fabric the thread representing Avogadro's rule has been rather loosely spun by us; but proper spinning yields the *same* thread, different only in that it is strong enough to be invulnerable to *all* doubts.

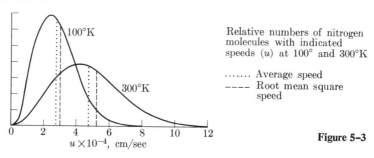

Relative numbers of nitrogen molecules with indicated speeds (u) at 100° and 300°K

.... Average speed
– – – – Root mean square speed

Figure 5–3

The Mass Spectrograph

Some half-century after Cannizzaro placed the scale of relative atomic weights on a firm basis, it at last became possible to confirm that scale by a completely independent method. This method uses data collected in the study of streams of gaseous ions which, when produced in a highly evacuated system, move substantially unperturbed by collisions. One can then observe and measure the deflections of the ions produced by controlled electromagnetic fields. An analysis of these deflections supports inferences about the masses of the ions.

In the apparatus sketched in Fig. 5–4, a trickle of (gaseous) sample enters through a capillary leak into a region in which some of the molecules are ionized by bombardment with low-energy electrons emitted by filament F. The ions so produced are drawn through slit S_1 by a weak electric field and are then powerfully accelerated through a potential drop of several thousand volts in the region between S_1 and S_2. Due to the Boltzmann distribution of thermal energies and, even more, to variations in the amount of energy acquired from the bombarding electrons, the ions passing through S_1 have a rather wide spread of energies. However, the accelerating potential between S_1 and S_2 is large enough to give every singly charged ion a *fixed* increment of energy roughly 100 times the largest energy it could possess at S_1. Hence the stream of ions emerging from slit S_2 is substantially homogeneous in translational kinetic energy—the magnitude of which can be calculated, with due attention to units, from the equation

$$\tfrac{1}{2}mu^2 = eV. \tag{a}$$

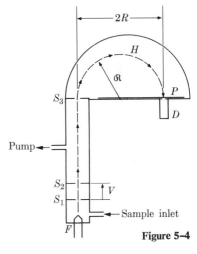

Figure 5–4

Here m and u are, respectively, the mass and velocity of the ion, V is the accelerating voltage, and e represents the charge on the ion (here assumed to have the magnitude of the unit of electronic charge).

The stream of high-energy ions is further collimated by passage through slit S_3. The narrow beam so produced then enters a region in which it is deflected by a powerful and uniform magnetic field (H) with lines of force running perpendicular to the plane of the paper. In this field the ions are constrained to follow a semicircular path, at the end of which they impinge on a photographic plate (P) which is locally blackened at the points of impingement.

From the position of the blackening on the plate and the geometry of the apparatus of which the plate is a part, one can infer the radius of curvature ($\Re$) of the semicircular path traversed by the ions in the magnetic field. This radius of curvature is, in turn, related to several other parameters by the equation

$$mu^2/\Re = Heu. \tag{b}$$

Here $mu^2/\Re$ expresses the centripetal force required to bend a particle having mass m and velocity u into a circular track with radius of curvature

$\mathcal{R}$. This centripetal constraint arises as the deflecting force *(Heu)* exerted by a magnetic field of strength H on a body with charge e proceeding with velocity u at right angles to the direction of the field. We have already seen that the velocity is primarily determined by the accelerating potential active in the region between S_1 and S_2. Rewriting equation (a), we find

$$u^2 = 2V \left(\frac{e}{m}\right). \tag{c}$$

An analogous rearrangement of equation (b) yields

$$\left(\frac{e}{m}\right) = \frac{u^2}{Hu\mathcal{R}} = \frac{u}{H\mathcal{R}} \quad \text{or} \quad \left(\frac{e}{m}\right)^2 = \frac{u^2}{H^2\mathcal{R}^2}.$$

Substituting now the value of u^2 given by equation (c), we obtain

$$\left(\frac{e}{m}\right)^2 = \frac{2V}{H^2\mathcal{R}^2} \cdot \left(\frac{e}{m}\right),$$

whence it follows that

$$\left(\frac{e}{m}\right) = \frac{2V}{H^2\mathcal{R}^2}.$$

We thus obtain an expression for the unknown charge-to-mass ratio of an ion in terms of three empirically determinable parameters: the accelerating voltage, the magnetic field strength, and the radius of curvature of the path followed by such an ion in the magnetic field.

Suppose that we introduce a trickle of gaseous hydrogen into a low-resolution mass spectrograph of the sort that was the best available up to about 1930. The photographic plate may then be blackened at several spots, for it is possible that beyond H^+ ions, such other species as H_2^+ will also be produced. However, it is not too difficult to identify the position of the blackening due to H^+ and—with the value of $\mathcal{R}$ so indicated and the known magnitudes of the electric and magnetic fields used—one thus obtains a value of e/m for hydrogen. There is no surprise in the value so obtained. To the accuracy of the experiment, it is quite satisfactorily consistent with the value we might perfectly well have predicted in advance, by dividing the unit of electronic charge (established in the Millikan oil-drop experiment, for example) by the absolute mass of the hydrogen atom calculated on p. 146.* But the crucial point is not so much quantitative

---

* The mass of an H^+ ion will of course differ from the mass of an H atom, by the margin of the mass of the electron removed in converting the atom to an ion. However, the mass of the electron is only about 1/2000 the mass of a hydrogen atom, so that (to the accuracy of the mass-spectrographic data here in question) the mass of the ion is quite satisfactorily approximated as the mass of the atom.

as qualitative. In framing our atomic theory, we stipulated that all atoms of a given element are characterized by some one particular mass, and the results obtained for hydrogen with a low-resolution mass spectrograph are entirely concordant with this stipulation.

If now we turn to such another element as nitrogen, we find that (when V and H are held constant) the blackened regions on the plate lie much farther to the right. This is exactly what we should expect. The more massive N^+ ion is much less readily deflected than the H^+ ion: the radius of curvature for the former $(\mathfrak{R}_n)$ must then be much greater than that for the latter $(\mathfrak{R}_h)$. Identifying the site of blackening due to the impingement of the N^+ ion, we can determine $\mathfrak{R}_n$ as formerly we determined $\mathfrak{R}_h$. And we can then write not only

$$\left(\frac{e}{m}\right)_h = \frac{2V}{H^2\mathfrak{R}_h^2}$$

but also

$$\left(\frac{e}{m}\right)_n = \frac{2V}{H^2\mathfrak{R}_n^2} .$$

For the ions H^+ and N^+ the charge (e) is the same. If we have taken care to maintain the constancy of H and V, these parameters are also the same in both cases. And then—even were we wholly ignorant of the numerical values of e, H, and V—we could still easily discover the *ratio* of the atomic masses of hydrogen and nitrogen, simply by combining the two above equations:

$$\frac{(e/m)_h}{(e/m)_n} = \frac{2V/H^2\mathfrak{R}_h^2}{2V/H^2\mathfrak{R}_n^2} ,$$

$$\frac{m_n}{m_h} = \left(\frac{\mathfrak{R}_n}{\mathfrak{R}_h}\right)^2 .$$

This remarkably simple equation puts us in a wonderful position. Consider that we work at constant values of V and H, and with ions having the same charge. To obtain the relative atomic masses we need then only determine the horizontal distance from the slit S_3 to the site of the blackening produced by each ion on the photographic plate. These distances represent the magnitude $2\mathfrak{R}$ (see Fig. 5–4). Now we see from the last equation that the ratio of the masses of the ions (and, very nearly, the ratio of the masses of the atoms) is simply the square of the ratio of the $2\mathfrak{R}$-distances measured for each of the species concerned. Thus, merely by making distance-measurements on photographic plates, we can confirm our previous conclusion that the ratio of the atomic mass of nitrogen to that of hydrogen is 14:1.* *At last* we have a strong confirmation of the whole chain of reasoning that Cannizzaro founded on Avogadro's rule and one supplementary assumption (see p. 83) which, though plausible, was not verifiable before. To say that we now have confirmation is *not* to imply that the mass spectrographic results are any more secure than those obtained on chemical grounds. The mass-spectrographic method has its own complexities and involves its own simplifying assumptions—of which we have said nothing. The crucial point is that we now have two completely *independent methods* that yield the *same results* when we proceed by entirely *different chains of reasoning* from entirely *different data*. In any one case such agreement may be dismissed as fortuitous, but, if it can be shown to obtain *generally*, our scale of relative atomic weights will have been placed on a very firm foundation indeed.

A large number of such confirmations can easily be obtained. If into our mass-spectrograph we introduce helium, for example, the site of blackening due to He^+ falls at a distance $(2\Re_{he})$ twice as great as $(2\Re_h)$—confirming our earlier conclusion that the atomic weights of helium and hydrogen stand in the ratio 4:1. Oxygen is somewhat difficult to handle in a mass spectrograph, but oxygenous compounds can be used to obtain results confirming the 16:1 ratio we earlier assigned as the ratio of the atomic weights of oxygen and hydrogen respectively. We can also establish a link with our reference standard, carbon, by introducing into the apparatus a gaseous carbon compound, e.g. methane (CH_4). We now find a mass spectrum of considerable complexity, corresponding to the presence

---

* Instead of using a photographic plate in a mass spectro*graph*, we may (generally do) prefer to use a mass spectro*meter* in which a single electronic ion detector (D in Fig. 5–4) is placed at a fixed distance $(2\Re_0)$ from S_3. By suitable adjustment of the accelerating voltage, any chosen ion (a) can be made to enter the narrow slit of this detector—the condition for such entry being given as follows:

$$(e/m)_a = 2V_a/H^2\Re_0^2.$$

To make a different ion (b) enter the detector, the accelerating voltage must be shifted to some different value determined by the similar equation

$$(e/m)_b = 2V_b/H^2\Re_0^2.$$

If then we work only with ions having the same charge (e), with fixed deflecting field (H), and with fixed detector distance $(2\Re_0)$, we can combine the last two equations to find

$$m_b/m_a = V_a/V_b.$$

The ratio of the particle masses is thus established in terms of an inverse ratio of measurable voltages. The results are entirely concordant with those obtained by the photographic technique.

of such species as CH_4^+, CH_4^{++}, CH_3^+, etc. But once we identify a spot as due to CH_4^+, say, we find that the distance $\Re_{ch_4}$ is 4 times $\Re_h$. If by definition we assign an atomic weight of 12 to carbon, it then follows that the relative atomic weight of hydrogen is 1, just as we earlier concluded.

Mixed in with this almost monotonous string of triumphs are also some surprises. With the element neon, to which gas-density methods assign an atomic weight of 20.18, we find *no* spot at the locus on the plate corresponding to a mass 20.18 times that of hydrogen. Instead, we find *two* spots, corresponding to masses 20 and 22—the first being considerably the stronger. However we purge our apparatus and however we introduce the neon sample, these two spots always show up, and with the same ratio of intensities: about 10:1. That ratio is itself suggestive. Suppose that ordinary neon actually consists of *two* species of atoms—some of mass 20 and some of mass 22—mixed in the proportion of 10 to 1, respectively. The *weighted average* mass in this mixture of atoms would be just 20.18 $\{= [10(20) + 1(22)]/11 = 222/11\}$, which *is* the value yielded by gas-density data. Is this only coincidence or an indication that our apparently wild supposition has hit the mark? If ordinary neon is a mixture of atoms with relative masses 20 and 22, one can readily imagine a procedure for at least partial separation of these *isotopes.** If we maintain a stream of ordinary neon inside a porous clay pipe, if we surround that pipe by a jacket that is continuously evacuated, and if we collect the (uneffused) neon arriving at the end of the pipe, this should be neon slightly enriched in the heavier isotope. For, by Graham's law, the rate at which the mass-20 isotope effuses through the walls of the pipe should be greater than the effusion rate for the mass-22 isotope, by the factor $\sqrt{22/20} = \sqrt{1.1} \doteq$ 1.05. Repeated recycling of the uneffused neon should then yield a specimen of neon appreciably enriched in the Ne^{22} isotope (because correspondingly depleted of Ne^{20} isotope). And, exactly as predicted, when we introduce into our mass spectrograph a specimen of neon thus produced, we find that the relative intensity of the blackening at the mass-22 locus is substantially increased.

Neon is not an isolated case. If we study chlorine (or, more easily, chlorine compounds) we find no blackening corresponding to what our chemical data would lead us to expect: a chlorine atom with mass ca. 35.5 times that of the hydrogen atom. Instead, we again find two spots—this time corresponding to masses 35 and 37, and having intensities that stand in the ratio 3:1 respectively. Again the chemical atomic weight is

---

* From Gr. *iso*, same + *topos*, place. Occupying the same position in the periodic table, the two isotopic species are quite different in mass, and are appropriately distinguished as Ne^{20} and Ne^{22}.

confirmed, insofar as the weighted average mass in this mixture is ca. 35.5 $\{= [3(35) + 1(37)]/4\}$, but *qualified* in that we must now regard ordinary chlorine as a mixture of two kinds of atoms no one of which actually has a mass 35.5 times that of hydrogen. This phenomenon of isotopism is actually one of very general occurrence. Ordinary tin, for example, has been found to consist of no fewer than 10 distinct isotopic species, corresponding to 10 different approximately integral atomic masses. The weighted average mass in this mixture is quite satisfactorily concordant with the chemical atomic weight of tin, 118.7, but there is *no* one tin atom with a relative mass of 118.7. Moreover, as the resolving power of mass-spectrographic equipment has been improved, we have been made aware of the existence of isotopic complexity even where it was not at first detected. Thus, though ordinary hydrogen consists predominantly of atoms with mass number 1, it also contains a small proportion of atoms with mass number 2 and a trace of (radioactive) atoms with mass number 3. Ordinary carbon is predominantly C^{12}, but contains some C^{13} and a trace of (radioactive) C^{14}; ordinary oxygen is predominantly O^{16}, but contains a small admixture of O^{17} and O^{18}; and so on.

How shall we react to the startlingly complex perspective opened up by these findings? One point that calls for immediate attention is the choice of a reference standard for the scale of relative atomic weights. The modern mass spectrometer is capable of supplying excellent values for the relative atomic weights of the chemical elements as they occur in nature. One determines, for each constituent isotope, a relative mass, which refined measurements show to differ significantly from the nearest integral number. And by weighting each such value according to the extent to which that isotope appears in the normal make-up of the element, one can obtain values of relative atomic weight that do not merely confirm but often surpass in accuracy the values assigned by traditional chemical methods. However, in carrying through such a mass-spectrometric determination, one will certainly wish to pin his scale of relative atomic masses to the standard constituted by assigning a number to some *one isotopic species*. In 1960 it was at last agreed that the mass-spectrometric scale should be based on an assignment of the number 12.00000 to the most abundant carbon isotope, C^{12}. In chemical atomic-weight work, on the other hand, one does not deal with pure C^{12} but, rather, with C^{12} containing an almost constant admixture of C^{13} and C^{14}. Mass spectrometry establishes that relative to $C^{12} = 12.00000$, the weighted-average atomic weight of the mixture is 12.01115. And so, by adopting 12.01115 as the atomic weight of the ordinary carbon that serves as the chemists' reference standard, we readily attain a *single consistent scale* of relative atomic weights, which can be based on *both* chemical and mass-spectrometric data.

The Concepts of Element and Compound

Many purely practical difficulties can easily be sidestepped as above, but we have yet to face a far more difficult problem of fundamental principle. How shall we revise our atomic theory in the light of this newly discovered complexity of the "chemical elements"?

One possibility is both very clear and very simple. **If** the mixture of isotopes characteristic of each "element" were absolutely the same everywhere in nature, and **if** laboratory operations made no change in the composition of any such mixture, there would be no problem at all. For we observed at the very outset that Lavoisier's concept of an "element"—as the last term at which analysis arrives—defines an element only in *relative* terms, i.e. with respect to a particular group of analytical techniques. Provided that the two above conditions were met, chemists might never use mass-spectrometric analyses, and could quite properly continue to regard the "chemical elements" *as* elements. Attractively simple, this is actually a grossly oversimplified point of view. The provisos on which it depends are today wholly inadmissible. For one thing, we find that the mixture of isotopes that constitutes a given "element" is certainly *not* absolutely invariant in nature. Certain elements (e.g. lead) show variations in isotopic composition large enough to be detected in a variability of the atomic weights determined by the classical methods of chemical analysis. The subsequent development of mass spectrometry confirms this finding and *generalizes* it. In *most* cases, different specimens of any given element found in nature will show variations in isotopic composition that are unmistakably detectable albeit very small—corresponding, for example, to variations in average atomic weight of ± 0.00001 for hydrogen, ± 0.00005 for carbon, ± 0.003 for sulfur, and so on. There is also a second major objection: chemical reactions *may* produce some separation of the isotopic components of a given element, with consequent change of its apparent atomic weight. And, by other techniques, we can produce an almost complete separation of pure isotopic species. These pure species play important roles in many purely chemical investigations, e.g. studies of reaction mechanisms, in which we make routine use of mass-spectrometric analysis. Thus it is *not* legitimate to leave this mode of analysis out of account when we consider the bearing of Lavoisier's definition on the situation we face today.

The simple first possibility having proved untenable, we turn to a second —which is also the second simplest. Adopting this view, we would revise our concept of "chemical element" to make each distinct isotopic species a distinct element. Ordinary "chemical hydrogen" is then regarded not as an element but as a *mixture* of isotopic elements (H^1, H^2, etc.); and each such isotopic element *is* characterized by its own invariant atomic weight, just as stipulated by the second postulate of our atomic theory (see p. 5). Ordinary water is then regarded not as a pure compound but as a *mixture* of isotopically distinct compounds like "light water" ($H_2^1O^{16}$), "heavy water" ($H_2^2O^{16}$), and such other compounds as $H_2^1O^{18}$. In light water, oxygen makes up eight-ninths of the total weight of the compound, while in heavy water it makes up only four-fifths of the total weight. Ordinary water will then show deviations from the law of definite proportions—dependent on the extent to which the various "waters" enter into the mixed sample at hand—but each isotopically distinct water *is* characterized by an invariant weight ratio, and does conform exactly to the law of definite proportions. Thus, the second point of view clearly offers a formally impeccable position on which we can always fall back. But it is *not* the position we ordinarily adopt.

The hydrogen isotopes *do*, after all, ordinarily present themselves in a substantially invariant proportion (N.B. only ±0.00001 variation in apparent atomic weight) and *do* show very nearly the same chemical properties. And, after all, the composition by weight of ordinary water *is* very nearly invariant, and all the isotopically distinct "compounds" present in ordinary water *are* very nearly the same in chemical properties. It is overwhelmingly convenient to consider as *one element* the isotopic mixture in which hydrogen ordinarily presents itself in nature, and as *one compound* the mixture of isotopically distinct species present in water as we ordinarily encounter it. Ordinarily it is both convenient and proper to regard *all* the familiar chemical elements as true elements and *all* the familiar compounds as true compounds. We are thus led to consider a third possibility, in some sense a compromise between the first two, which duly combines the *possibility* of logical impeccability with the *actuality* of pragmatic usefulness. *Ordinarily* we can with advantage act upon the traditional view of elements and compounds. But in *extraordinary* circumstances—for example, when we use pure heavy water as a distinct species—we are perfectly free to fall back on what is in fact our *ultimate* position, from which we regard as distinct the species expressly distinguished as $H_2^1O^{16}$, $H_2^2O^{16}$, etc. We can thus retain and exploit the familiar scale of relative atomic weights, and the familiar assignments of empirical and molecular formulas, even while holding ourselves ready to abandon them for a more discriminating scale of isotopic weights and a more discriminating assignment of different formulas to isotopically distinct compounds.

Does the adoption of the third possibility outlined above entail an unforgivable sacrifice of logical tidiness to practical expediency? Not at all! In science just this kind of compromise view seems often to represent an optimal choice. Consider, for example, our attitude toward the relation of classical and relativistic dynamics. As a first possibility, we could stubbornly refuse to take account of the work of Einstein and others, and simply defend classical dynamics in its traditional domain. This possibility hobbles us within the domain of classical physics and is unacceptable for this reason. As a second possibility, we might make a thoroughgoing adoption of relativistic dynamics. But calculations performed simply and correctly in classical dynamics become almost impossibly difficult when we try to conduct them by the methods of relativistic dynamics. We are thus led to choose a third possibility, a compromise position. *Ordinarily* (i.e. in classical contexts) we feel entirely free to use the convenient concepts and methods of classical dynamics, but in *extraordinary* circumstances (i.e. nonclassical contexts) we adopt the more difficult but more adequate concepts of relativistic dynamics. Our attitude here parallels almost exactly the attitude of modern users of the chemical atomic theory, as sketched above. This attitude is not only permissible but desirable. For, after all, a sterile logical impeccability is not the prime desideratum in a scientific theory. The criterion of excellence in a scientific theory is its capacity to lead us to important new discoveries. The atomic theory described in this book continues to serve today—as did its less sophisticated ancestors in ages past—as a pointer to many landmark discoveries in our continuing exploration of the world of nature.

Illustrative Example. Ammonia under a pressure of 15 atm at 27°C is heated to 347°C in a closed vessel containing also some catalyst. The vessel maintains effectively constant volume, and the pressure mounts to 50 atm. Neglecting deviations from the ideal gas laws, calculate:

(a) the pressure the ammonia would exert were it to remain wholly undecomposed;

(b) the percentage of the ammonia actually decomposed according to the reaction $2NH_3 = N_2 + 3H_2$.

Amontons' law for constant-volume systems gives us

$$P_1/T_1 = P_2/T_2.$$

Converting from centigrade to Kelvin temperatures, we may write

$$15/300 = P_0/620,$$

where P_0 is the pressure the ammonia would have exerted had it been entirely undecomposed. We thus find

$$P_0 = 31 \text{ atm.} \tag{a}$$

The actual pressure is higher, by 19 atm, than the calculated pressure. Looking at the equation for the decomposition reaction, we see that 4 gaseous molecules are formed for each 2 gaseous molecules (of ammonia) decomposed. Were we working in a system maintained at *constant pressure* then, by Avogadro's rule, two volumes of the gaseous products would appear for each volume of ammonia decomposed. A moment's reflection on Avogadro's rule and Dalton's law leads to the conclusion that—working as we are at *constant volume*—2 atm pressure of gaseous products should be formed for each 1 atm of ammonia decomposed. Let p_d represent the pressure, in atmospheres, of the ammonia actually decomposed. Then we may write

pressure of undecomposed ammonia + pressure of decomposition products = total pressure.

The pressure of undecomposed ammonia is plainly $= P_0 - p_d$.

The pressure of the decomposition products

$$= 2 \times \text{pressure of ammonia decomposed} = 2p_d.$$

Substituting in the first equation on this page, we find

$$(P_0 - p_d) + 2p_d = \text{total pressure,}$$

whence

$$(31 - p_d) + 2p_d = 50 \quad \text{or} \quad p_d = 50 - 31 = 19\,\text{atm.}$$

Of the 31 atm of ammonia that would have been present in the absence of any decomposition, 19 atm are actually decomposed. Therefore

$$\% \text{ ammonia decomposed} = \tfrac{19}{31} \times 100 = 61\%. \tag{b}$$

Note that in this simple case, in which two molecules of products are formed for each molecule of starting material decomposed, the difference between the actual total pressure and the calculated pressure is numerically equal to the pressure of that part of the starting material which decomposes.

Illustrative Example. The molal boiling-point elevation of water is 0.510°C. Under 1 atm pressure a $0.1M$ aqueous solution of the weak acid HA boils at 100.0561°C.

(a) How many moles of "particles" (ions and molecules) are present in one liter of solution?

(b) What fraction of the HA molecules is dissociated?

For aqueous solutions the general equation $K_B m = \Delta T_B$ becomes

$$0.510 \times \text{molality of solution} = \text{rise of boiling point over } 100°C.$$

In the present case we have

$$0.510 \times m = 0.0561, \quad m = 0.11.$$

This calculated molality refers to the number of moles per 1000 *gm of solvent* but, *in dilute aqueous solutions*, the same figure well approximates the number of moles per 1000 *ml of solution*. We may, therefore, say that the number of moles of "particles" in 1 liter of the solution is 0.11.

For every one HA "particle" dissociated, two "particles" (H^+ and A^- ions) are produced—so that the situation here exactly parallels that noted at the end of the last example. And then we easily see how to base a calculation of all the equilibrium concentrations on the observation that, instead of the 0.1 mole of HA put in, a total concentration of 0.11 mole of $HA + H^+ + A^-$ is present at equilibrium:

$$\text{moles of } H^+ = \text{moles of } A^- = \text{moles HA dissociated} = 0.11 - 0.10 = 0.01,$$
$$\text{moles of HA remaining} = 0.10 - 0.01 = 0.09$$

As a check, note that the total concentration of $HA + H^+ + A^- = 0.09 + 0.01 + 0.01 = 0.11$ exactly as required. Thus we can be sure that, of the 0.1 mole of HA put in, 0.01 mole is dissociated. Consequently:

$$\text{fraction of HA molecules dissociated} = \frac{0.01}{0.1} = \frac{1}{10}.$$

PROBLEMS

1. The molal freezing-point-depression constant for water is 1.86°. At 0.01 molal solution of the weak acid HA in water is found to freeze at $-0.0223°C$. Calculate
   (a) the number of moles of "particles" (ions and molecules) in the solution,
   (b) the percent dissociation of the acid HA.

2. At $-33.4°C$, the boiling point of pure ammonia, a 2.82 percent (by weight) solution of potassium amide (KNH_2) in liquid ammonia has a vapor pressure of 746.7 mm Hg. Calculate, approximately, the degree of ionization of KNH_2 in this solution. (Atomic weights: H, 1; N, 14; K, 39.)

3. Nitrogen tetroxide (N_2O_4) may dissociate according to the equation $N_2O_4 = 2NO_2$. In discussing this dissociation, we will let M_0 represent the molecular weight of pure N_2O_4, α the fraction of the N_2O_4 that is dissociated to NO_2 under some particular conditions of temperature and pressure, and M the apparent (average) molecular weight of the N_2O_4–NO_2 mixture so produced.
   (a) Show that $M = M_0/(1 + \alpha)$.
   (b) For nitrogen tetroxide $M_0 = 92$, but at 27°C and 1 atm pressure the apparent molecular weight of nitrogen tetroxide is 76.8. Calculate the fraction of the N_2O_4 dissociated under these conditions.
   (c) Were N_2O_4 wholly undissociated, its density (δ_0) and molecular weight (M_0) would be related by the equation

   $$\delta_0 = PM_0/RT.$$

   Letting δ represent the density of N_2O_4 — NO_2 mixture produced by partial dissociation of the N_2O_4, show that

   $$\delta = \frac{PM_0}{RT(1 + \alpha)}.$$

4. Nitrosyl bromide (NOBr) may decompose according to the equation $2NOBr = 2NO + Br_2$. In discussing this decomposition, we will let M_0

represent the molecular weight ($=110$) of pure NOBr, α the fraction of the NOBr that is decomposed under some particular conditions of temperature and pressure, and δ the measured density of the gas mixture existing under those conditions.

(a) Assuming that all species are present as gases and noting that in this case the fragments are *not* the same in molecular weight, demonstrate that

$$\delta = \frac{PM_0}{RT(1 + \alpha/2)}.$$

(b) A 500-ml flask was charged with 0.55 gm of pure NOBr. When the flask was brought to room temperature (293°K), the contents of the flask were found to be wholly gaseous and to exert a total pressure of 0.34 atm. Calculate the fraction of the NOBr that is decomposed under these conditions.

5. (a) By high-temperature treatment with excess sulfur (atomic weight 32.06), just 1.0000 gm of metallic copper (atomic weight 63.54) was converted to a copper sulfide, of which 1.2561 gm were obtained. What is the ratio of copper to sulfur atoms in this copper sulfide?

(b) The experimental results cited in (a) were obtained in a carefully conducted experiment and should be good to ±0.0002 gm. What interpretation will you then place on the result of your calculation in (a)?

(c) Conceivably, a *trace* of air may have leaked into the system used in obtaining the results cited in (a). The reaction of the oxygen (atomic weight 16.00) thus introduced may have yielded, instead of the expected pure copper sulfide, a mixture of copper sulfide with a *trace* of cupric oxide (CuO). Would the possible presence of this *trace* impurity suffice to explain the deviation of the ratio calculated in (a) from an exact ratio of small whole numbers?

6. (a) One may wonder exactly how it comes about that the Perrin experiment permits us to evaluate Avogadro's number. Consider this proposition: the larger Avogadro's number, the smaller the maximum size of a particle that shows Brownian motion. Explain the basis for this proposition, and then use the proposition to offer some rationale for the success of the Perrin experiment.

(b) In a Perrin-style experiment, use was made of a suspension of uniform spherical particles of gamboge (density 1.206 gm/cm³) in water at 15°C (density 0.999 gm/cm³). These particles (having a radius of 0.0000226 cm) were found to distribute themselves in such fashion that for every 100 particles counted per unit volume of the suspension at some horizontal plane, only 47 particles are counted per unit volume in a horizontal plane just 0.003 cm vertically higher than the first in the experimental cell. That is, the ratio of particle concentrations is 2.13 ($=100/47$), and the same ratio is found between the particle concentrations at any pair of horizontal planes 0.003 cm apart in the cell. From these data calculate a value for Avogadro's number. Considering the accuracy of the data given, should one expect any more accurate result? ($R = 8.31 \times 10^7$ ergs/ mole-°K; $g = 980$ cm/sec^2.)

7. (a) The planet Pfuionid has an isothermal atmosphere containing only hydrogen (molecular weight, 2) and neon (molecular weight, 20). At the surface of the planet each of these gases exerts a partial pressure of 1000 mm. At some particular altitude in the atmosphere of Pfuionid the partial pressure of hydrogen has declined to 100 mm. What is the partial pressure of neon at this altitude?

(b) Assume our own atmosphere fully isothermal and subject to the constraints of the Boltzmann distribution law. At sea level the total pressure of 1.0 atm is exerted by a gas mixture consisting of nitrogen and oxygen in the molar ratio of, roughly, 4:1. To one significant figure, what is (i) the value of the molar ratio and (ii) the total pressure (in atmospheres) at an altitude of 20 miles?

(Molecular weight: O_2, 32; N_2, 28; $g = 980$ cm/sec^2; $R = 8.3 \times 10^7$ ergs/ mole-°K; 1 mile $= 1.6 \times 10^5$ cm.)

8. Only a trifling knowledge of the calculus is required to obtain the equation (first derived by Svedberg in 1925) that permits determination of molecular weight from the observable sedimentation equilibrium of macromolecules in a centrifugal field.

(a) Consider that we centrifuge, in a horizontal plane, a solution of some substance with unknown molecular mass m. At any distance r from the axis of rotation, a body with mass m is acted upon by a "force" $= mu^2/r$, where u is the body's instantaneous linear velocity. Show that this "force" can be expressed as $m\omega^2 r$, where ω is the (readily measurable) angular velocity of the rotor in radians per second.

(b) The mass of the liquid medium displaced by one solute molecule at first seems wholly indeterminate since, though the density ρ of the medium is readily measurable, we see no way to establish the effective volume of one molecule. However, with a dilatometer one can easily measure the specific volume $\bar{v}$ representing the increase in volume produced by the addition of one gram of the solute to a large volume of the solution. Show that the mass of the medium displaced by one solute molecule $= m\bar{v}\rho$.

(c) The *net* force acting on each solute molecule is the difference between the "force" due to the centrifugal field, acting to drive the molecule *away* from the axis of rotation, and a lesser buoyant force acting to drive the molecule toward the free surface of the solution, i.e., *toward* the axis of rotation. By Archimedes' principle, the buoyant force is equal to the "weight" of the medium displaced—which, in effect, means the mass of the displaced medium times the local acceleration. Show that the net force acting on the solute molecule $= m(1 - \bar{v}\rho)\omega^2 r$.

(d) To bring the particle an infinitesimal distance dr closer to the axis of rotation demands the investment of work expressible as $m(1 - \bar{v}\rho)\omega^2 r\, dr$. Because the force clearly changes as a function of r, an integration is required to determine the total work required to bring the particle from some original distance $r = r_0$ to $r = 0$ at the axis of rotation. Show that the magnitude of the total work required is $m(1 - \bar{v}\rho)\omega^2 r_0^2/2$.

(e) The positional potential energy ϵ of the molecule we may define as zero when $r = 0$, i.e., when the molecule stands at the axis of rotation. When the molecule stands at distance $r = r_0$ its potential energy is thus expressible as $-m(1 - \bar{v}\rho)\omega^2 r_0^2/2$: why is the minus sign present?

(f) With due attention to signs, express the change of potential energy, $\Delta\epsilon$, of the molecule when it is moved from distance $r = r_1$ to distance $r = r_2$, where $r_2 > r_1$. By substituting this expression in Boltzmann's law, show that the corresponding numbers of molecules at the two positions, η_1 and η_2, are related by the equation

$$\eta_2/\eta_1 = e^{+m(1-\bar{v}\rho)\omega^2(r_2^2-r_1^2)/2kT}.$$

Is η_2 greater or less than η_1, and how do you account for this situation?

(g) The ratio η_2/η_1 is spectrophotometrically determinable when equilibrium has been established in the centrifuge. Show that, with this ratio in hand, one can calculate the molecular weight, M, of the solute from the following relation:

$$M = \frac{2RT \ln \eta_2/\eta_1}{(1 - \bar{v}\rho)\omega^2(r_2^2 - r_1^2)}.$$

APPENDIXES

The familiar denary logarithm (symbolized log) is a logarithm to the base 10 and satisfies the defining condition

$$10^{\log x} = x.$$

The natural logarithm referred to in these appendixes (and symbolized ln) is a logarithm to the base e, where $e = 2.71828\ldots$, and satisfies the defining condition

$$(2.718)^{\ln x} = e^{\ln x} = x.$$

Given this similarity of definition, we can manipulate natural and denary logarithms in much the same way. Just as $\log (y)^z = z \log y$, for example, so also does $\ln (y)^z = z \ln y$. Also, just as $a = 10^x$ is exactly equivalent to $\log a = x$, so also is $b = e^x$ exactly equivalent to $\ln b = x$.

We easily shift from one logarithmic scale to the other. By definition, $x = 10^{\log x}$; and, taking the natural logarithms, we find

$$\ln x = \ln (10^{\log x}) = \log x \cdot \ln 10.$$

The natural logarithm of 10 is $2.303\ldots$, so that

$$\ln x = 2.303 \log x.$$

We may just state at this point one relation, involving natural logarithms, which will be useful in what follows. If by β we define some number less than 1, then

$$\ln \frac{1}{1 - \beta} = \ln (1 + \beta + \beta^2 + \beta^3 + \cdots) = \beta + \frac{\beta^2}{2} + \frac{\beta^3}{3} + \cdots$$

When β is *much* less than 1, all the higher-power terms in β become negligible and, in this special case, the following is an excellent approximation:

$$\ln \frac{1}{1 - \beta} = \beta.$$

LAWS FOR BOILING-POINT ELEVATION AND FREEZING-POINT DEPRESSION

If T_B is the boiling point of the pure solvent, under any particular pressure P^0, the vapor pressure of solvent over the solution reaches this value only at some higher temperature T_B^*, as shown in Fig. A1–1. Assuming that the solution is ideal, the vapor pressure corresponding to point A will, by Raoult's law, be $P^0 X_v$, where X_v is the mole fraction of solvent in the particular solution at issue. Moreover, if the solution is ideal, the slope of the line AC will be equal to the slope of the (log P vs. $1/T$)-line for the pure solvent—and thus equal to $-\Delta H_{\mathrm{vap}}/2.3R$, where ΔH_{vap} is the molar heat of vaporization of the pure solvent.

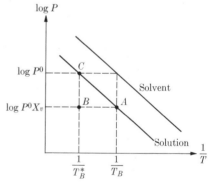

Now we can of course also express the slope of the line AC as "rise-over-run," and write

$$\text{slope } AC = \frac{BC}{AB}.$$

Hence

$$-\frac{\Delta H_{\mathrm{vap}}}{2.3R} = \frac{\log P^0 - \log P^0 X_v}{1/T_B^* - 1/T_B}$$

$$= \frac{\log (1/X_v)}{(T_B - T_B^*)/T_B T_B^*}.$$

Figure A1–1

Now, $T_B^* - T_B$ is simply the boiling point elevation, ΔT_B; and the product $T_B T_B^*$ can be well approximated as $(T_B)^2$ if the solution is highly dilute, so that the term T_B^* differs comparatively slightly from T_B. We have then

$$\frac{\Delta H_{\mathrm{vap}}}{2.3 R T_B^2} = \frac{\log (1/X_v)}{\Delta T_B}.$$

Substituting $(1 - X_u)$ for X_v, and recalling that 2.3 is the factor that converts natural to denary logarithms, we find that

$$\frac{\Delta H_{\text{vap}}}{RT_B^2} = \frac{\ln\left[1/(1 - X_u)\right]}{\Delta T_B}.$$

Having stipulated that the solution is highly dilute, i.e. that $X_u \ll 1$, we can get rid of the logarithmic term by using the approximation given above, and the last equation then becomes

$$\frac{\Delta H_{\text{vap}}}{RT_B^2} = \frac{X_u}{\Delta T_B}.$$

Invoking for the third and last time the diluteness of the solution, we can use the approximation given on p. 109 to substitute for X_u the expression $mM/1000$, where m is the molality of the *solute* and M is the molecular weight of the solvent. We then write

$$\frac{\Delta H_{\text{vap}}}{RT_B^2} = \frac{mM/1000}{\Delta T_B}$$

and arrive thence at the expression written on p. 123:

$$\Delta T_B = \frac{RT_B^2 M}{1000\,\Delta H_{\text{vap}}}\, m.$$

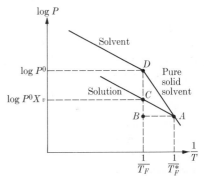

Figure A1–2

The derivation of the freezing-point-depression relation proceeds by way of an exactly parallel train of argument. We wish to relate the slope of the line AD to the "run" AB and the "rise" BD. Our first task is to find an expression for the latter—which we do by considering BC and CD separately. The slope of AC is, as before, $-\Delta H_{\text{vap}}/2.3R$, where ΔH_{vap} is the molar heat of vaporization of solvent from the (ideal) solution. The distance AB is $1/T_F - 1/T_F^*$, where T_F is the freezing point of the pure solvent and T_F^* is the freezing point of the solution. Hence we can solve for the distance BC from the equations

$$\text{slope } AC = \frac{BC}{AB}, \qquad -\frac{\Delta H_{\text{vap}}}{2.3R} = \frac{BC}{1/T_F - 1/T_F^*},$$

$$BC = -\frac{\Delta H_{\text{vap}}}{2.3R} \cdot \frac{T_F^* - T_F}{T_F T_F^*} = \frac{\Delta H_{\text{vap}}\,\Delta T_F}{2.3RT_F^2},$$

where ΔT_F, the actual freezing-point depression, is expressed as a *positive* number $= T_F - T_F^*$. Turning now to the length CD, we can write

$$CD = \log P^0 - \log P^0 X_v = \log(1/X_v),$$

where P^0 is the pressure of the vapor over the pure solvent at its melting point. Finally, we observe that the slope of the line AD is $-\Delta H_{\text{sub}}/2.3R$, where ΔH_{sub} is the molar heat of sublimation from the pure solid solvent. And now we can write

$$\text{slope } AD = \frac{BD}{AB} = \frac{BC + CD}{AB}.$$

Substituting, we obtain

$$-\frac{\Delta H_{\text{sub}}}{2.3R} = \frac{\Delta H_{\text{vap}} \Delta T_F/2.3RT_F^2 + \log(1/X_v)}{-\Delta T_F/T_F^2},$$

whence

$$\log \frac{1}{X_v} = \frac{\Delta T_F}{2.3RT_F^2}(\Delta H_{\text{sub}} - \Delta H_{\text{vap}}).$$

How shall we interpret this difference of heat terms? To go in one step from solid to vapor, we invest the heat of sublimation (ΔH_{sub}). To go in two steps from solid to vapor, we first invest the molar heat of fusion (ΔH_{fus}) to melt the solid, and then the heat of vaporization (ΔH_{vap}) to volatilize the liquid. Noting that the net effect is exactly the same whichever route is followed, we conclude that (if all changes are conducted at constant pressure) the heat investments along the two paths must be exactly the same. That is,

$$\Delta H_{\text{fus}} + \Delta H_{\text{vap}} = \Delta H_{\text{sub}} \quad \text{or} \quad \Delta H_{\text{fus}} = \Delta H_{\text{sub}} - \Delta H_{\text{vap}}.$$

Substitution in the earlier equation then yields

$$\log \frac{1}{X_v} = \frac{\Delta T_F \, \Delta H_{\text{fus}}}{2.3RT_F^2}.$$

The same series of substitutions and approximations then serves to carry us to the equation given on p. 123:

$$\Delta T_F = \frac{RT_F^2 M}{1000 \, \Delta H_{\text{fus}}} \, m.$$

THE OSMOTIC-PRESSURE LAW

In the apparatus shown in Fig. A 2–1 the solution in the right arm and the pure solvent in the left are linked through the vapor phase with which both are in contact. The vapor pressure of the solution is, of course, less than the vapor pressure of the pure solvent. Yet we find experimentally that there is *no net transfer* from solvent to solution, as in the case noted on p. 120. How can this be? The vapor pressures are indeed different, but observe that the vapor pressure of the solution is exerted at a greater altitude in the system than that at which the larger vapor pressure of the pure solvent is exerted. Now if the difference in altitude (h) were such that the two vapor pressures just fitted the demands of the barometric formula, then indeed we *would* have a genuine equilibrium system in which there would be no net transfer of vapor from solvent to solution (or conversely). Turning the argument around, we say that—since we find experimentally that the system *is* in equilibrium—the barometric formula *must* express the relation of the two vapor pressures and the height h. Once given this conclusion, the derivation of the osmotic-pressure law presents no problem in principle.

The osmotic pressure (π) indicated in our system is given by the expression

$$\pi = \rho g h.$$

Here ρ is the density of the solution in question, g is the gravitational acceleration, and π is then expressed not in such empirical units as cm Hg, etc. but, rather, in units of dynes. Let us denote by $\overline{V}$ the volume occupied by one gram-molecular weight (M) of pure solvent: the density of the pure solvent is then readily expressed as $M/\overline{V}$. If the solution is dilute, its

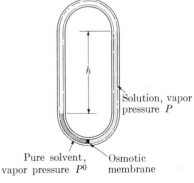

Solution, vapor pressure P

Pure solvent, vapor pressure P^0

Osmotic membrane

Figure A2–1

density will not differ appreciably from that of the pure solvent, in which case we can write $\rho \doteq M/\overline{V}$. Substituting, we find that

$$\pi\overline{V} = Mgh. \tag{1}$$

So far we have used only our definition of osmotic pressure and an approximation based on the stipulated diluteness of the solution. At this point we bring to bear the barometric formula, as it appears on p. 150. In the terms of our present discussion, we can rewrite our equation as

$$P/P^0 = e^{-Mgh/RT},$$

where P^0 is the vapor pressure of the pure solvent and P is the vapor pressure of the solution standing a distance h above the surface of the pure solvent. Taking the natural logarithm of both sides of the last equation, we write

$$\ln \frac{P}{P^0} = - \frac{Mg}{RT} h.$$

Assuming that the solution is ideal, we can invoke Raoult's law to write $P = P^0 X_v$, or $P/P^0 = X_v$. Substitution then yields

$$\ln X_v = - \frac{Mgh}{RT}, \qquad \ln \frac{1}{X_v} = \frac{Mgh}{RT}.$$

By substituting from equation (1) we then obtain

$$\ln \frac{1}{X_v} = \frac{\pi\overline{V}}{RT}. \tag{2}$$

This equation offers a fair representation of the behavior of appreciably concentrated solutions. If now we stipulate *extreme* diluteness of the solution, we can proceed as in Appendix 1, writing

$$\frac{\pi\overline{V}}{RT} = \ln \frac{1}{X_v} = \ln \frac{1}{1 - X_u} \doteq X_u \doteq \frac{n_u}{n_v}.$$

Since the solution has been stipulated *very* dilute, we have (in the last step) gone on to express the mole fraction as the ratio of the number of moles of solute present (n_u) to the number of moles of solvent present (n_v). But now $\overline{V}$ is the volume occupied by one mole of solvent and n_v is the number of moles of solvent present, whence it follows that the total volume (V) of the highly dilute solution is given as $V = \overline{V}n_v$. Making this substitution in our last equation, we obtain

$$\frac{\pi V}{RT} = n_u.$$

At this point we have demonstrated that *in very dilute solution*, the osmotic-pressure law has exactly the same form as the ideal gas law. Thus, the expression suggested first only as a speculation, and later established only as an empirical relation, has at last been given a convincing theoretical *derivation*. Observe further that we can, if we wish, leave π expressed in units of dynes, but then R must also be expressed in the same units. If, on the other hand, we wish to use 6.23 as the value of R, we must express π in cm Hg (and V in liters). Observe finally that just as in Chapter 4, we can take the quotient n_u/V as equal to the molar concentration of solute (c). We will then write

$$\pi = cRT,$$

which is the now familiar equation used on pp. 131 *et seq.*

Table of Atomic Weights 1961 (Based on Carbon-12)

Element	Symbol	Atomic number	Atomic weight[1]
Actinium	Ac	89	(227)
Aluminum	Al	13	26.9815
Americium	Am	95	241*(243)
Antimony	Sb	51	121.75
Argon	Ar	18	39.948
Arsenic	As	33	74.9216
Astatine	At	85	(210)
Barium	Ba	56	137.34
Berkelium	Bk	97	249*(247)
Beryllium	Be	4	9.0122
Bismuth	Bi	83	208.980
Boron	B	5	10.811
Bromine	Br	35	79.909
Cadmium	Cd	48	112.40
Calcium	Ca	20	40.08
Californium	Cf	98	252*(251)
Carbon	C	6	12.01115
Cerium	Ce	58	140.12
Cesium	Cs	55	132.905
Chlorine	Cl	17	35.453
Chromium	Cr	24	51.996
Cobalt	Co	27	58.9332
Copper	Cu	29	63.54
Curium	Cm	96	242*(247)
Dysprosium	Dy	66	162.50
Einsteinium	Es	99	(254)
Erbium	Er	68	167.26
Europium	Eu	63	151.96
Fermium	Fm	100	(253)
Fluorine	F	9	18.9984
Francium	Fr	87	(223)
Gadolinium	Gd	64	157.25
Gallium	Ga	31	69.72
Germanium	Ge	32	72.59
Gold	Au	79	196.967
Hafnium	Hf	72	178.49
Helium	He	2	4.0026
Holmium	Ho	67	164.930
Hydrogen	H	1	1.00797
Indium	In	49	114.82
Iodine	I	53	126.9044
Iridium	Ir	77	192.2
Iron	Fe	26	55.847
Krypton	Kr	36	83.80
Lanthanum	La	57	138.91
Lead	Pb	82	207.19
Lithium	Li	3	6.939
Lutetium	Lu	71	174.97
Magnesium	Mg	12	24.312
Manganese	Mn	25	54.9380
Mendelevium	Md	101	(256)
Mercury	Hg	80	200.59
Molybdenum	Mo	42	95.94
Neodymium	Nd	60	144.24
Neon	Ne	10	20.183
Neptunium	Np	93	(237)
Nickel	Ni	28	58.71
Niobium	Nb	41	92.906
Nitrogen	N	7	14.0067
Nobelium	No	102	(254)
Osmium	Os	76	190.2
Oxygen	O	8	15.9994
Palladium	Pd	46	106.4
Phosphorus	P	15	30.9738
Platinum	Pt	78	195.09
Plutonium	Pu	94	239*(244)
Polonium	Po	84	210*(209)
Potassium	K	19	39.102
Praseodymium	Pr	59	140.907
Promethium	Pm	61	147*(145)
Protactinium	Pa	91	(231)
Radium	Ra	88	(226)
Radon	Rn	86	(222)
Rhenium	Re	75	186.2
Rhodium	Rh	45	102.905
Rubidium	Rb	37	85.47
Ruthenium	Ru	44	101.07
Samarium	Sm	62	150.35
Scandium	Sc	21	44.956
Selenium	Se	34	78.96
Silicon	Si	14	28.086
Silver	Ag	47	107.870
Sodium	Na	11	22.9898
Strontium	Sr	38	87.62
Sulfur	S	16	32.064
Tantalum	Ta	73	180.948
Technetium	Tc	43	99*(97)
Tellurium	Te	52	127.60
Terbium	Tb	65	158.924
Thallium	Tl	81	204.37
Thorium	Th	90	232.038
Thulium	Tm	69	168.934
Tin	Sn	50	118.69
Titanium	Ti	22	47.90
Tungsten	W	74	183.85
Uranium	U	92	238.03
Vanadium	V	23	50.942
Xenon	Xe	54	131.30
Ytterbium	Yb	70	173.04
Yttrium	Y	39	88.905
Zinc	Zn	30	65.37
Zirconium	Zr	40	91.22

[1] For elements available only as radionuclides produced artificially or by decay of longer-lived radionuclides, the mass number of the longest-lived known isotope is listed in parentheses, and the isotope most readily available for chemical experimentation is listed with an asterisk if it differs from the isotope in parentheses.

Index